WORDBOOK 7

Johnson O'Connor Research Foundation, Inc.
Vocabulary Building Program

By Richard Bowker

Vocabulary Scale 7775–8375
(Old VS 170–202)

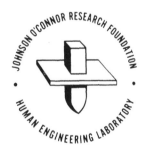

Johnson O'Connor Research Foundation, Inc.

Atlanta • Boston • Chicago • Dallas • Denver • Houston
Los Angeles • New York • San Francisco • Seattle • Washington, D.C.

10/11

WORDBOOK
347 Beacon Street
Boston, MA 02116
(800) 355–3670

books@jocrf.org

The Johnson O'Connor Research Foundation, Inc. is a nonprofit scientific and research organization with two primary commitments: to study human abilities and to provide people with a knowledge of their aptitudes that will help them in making decisions about school and work. Since 1922, hundreds of thousands of people have used our service to learn more about themselves and to derive more satisfaction from their lives. The Foundation has offices in major cities across the nation. For more information about the aptitude testing program, go to http://www.jocrf.org, or contact any of our offices below.

Atlanta	(404) 261–8013	atlanta@jocrf.org
Boston	(617) 536–0409	boston@jocrf.org
Chicago	(312) 787–9141	chicago@jocrf.org
Dallas	(972) 991–8378	dallas@jocrf.org
Denver	(303) 388–5600	denver@jocrf.org
Houston	(713) 462–5562	houston@jocrf.org
Los Angeles	(213) 817-6625	la@jocrf.org
New York	(212) 269–0550	ny@jocrf.org
San Francisco	(415) 772–9030	sf@jocrf.org
Seattle	(206) 623–4070	seattle@jocrf.org
Washington, D.C.	(202) 828–8378	washdc@jocrf.org

Contents

Pronunciation Key   **inside front cover**

How to Use This Book   **iv**

Chapter 1   **1**

Chapter 2   **7**

Chapter 3   **13**

Review Test 1   **19**

Chapter 4   **21**

Chapter 5   **27**

Chapter 6   **33**

Review Test 2   **39**

Chapter 7   **41**

Chapter 8   **47**

Chapter 9   **53**

Review Test 3   **59**

Chapter 10   **61**

Chapter 11   **67**

Chapter 12   **73**

Review Test 4   **79**

Common Prefixes   **81**

Common Suffixes   **83**

Answers   **85**

Index   **90**

Vocabulary Review List   **91**

How to Use This Book

This book has been written to help you increase your knowledge of words. It does this by discussing and testing you on words that are at a certain level of difficulty on our vocabulary scale. You have probably already taken a test which showed you where you score on this scale. If you study the words which are about at your level, they should be easier for you to learn than words that are much higher on the scale.

There are many different ways of using this book. If you are studying vocabulary as part of a class, your teacher may tell you the best way he or she has found to use it. If you are studying on your own, here are some suggestions:

Start at the beginning of the book, even if it is below your vocabulary scale score. If you do not know some words below that level you certainly should learn them, and they should not be too difficult to learn.

The first step in studying a chapter is to take the Pretest. This will tell you what words you do not know. You should certainly study any words you get wrong on this Pretest. Since it is possible to get an item right by guessing, you should also make a note of any words you aren't quite sure of; study them even if you get them right.

Next, read over the discussion of each word you missed or weren't sure of. Memorize its meaning. Pay careful attention to the way the word is used in the sample sentences. Try to get a *feel* for the word. Use a dictionary (or two) in addition to reading the discussion. Try to understand the other forms which the word may take. (The lists of prefixes and suffixes at the end of the book can be very helpful for this.) When you think you know the word, go on to the exercises.

The exercises give you three ways of testing your understanding of the word. They do not have to be done in any particular order. If you make a mistake on any one of them, though, you should go back and reread the discussion for that word. After every three chapters there is a review section for words in those chapters. Any words you get wrong on this review section should, of course, be restudied.

You might want to work with the test words in other ways as well. Have someone read the words aloud to you; see if you can recognize them and write them correctly. Try to write a composition that uses all of the words. See if you can write good definitions of the words without looking at the discussions or a dictionary.

Once you think you have learned the words in a chapter, go on to the next one. It is a good idea, though, to make a list or keep a notebook of the words you have learned so that you can review them from time to time. As you go through the book you may find the words becoming slightly more difficult. This will be particularly true as you go beyond your score on the vocabulary scale. If you get to a point where you are missing about half the words in a chapter, you should slow down and spend more time with each word. It would also be a good idea to begin studying the words that you got right on the Pretest, in order to fix them more firmly in your mind.

By the time you finish this book we hope that all the words in it will be a part of your vocabulary. At that point you should be ready to learn more words that are harder than these. You should continue to review these words, however, until you know them so well that they are a natural part of your speech and writing.

Chapter 1

Pretest

Each test word is printed in CAPITAL letters. From the five choices on the next line, select the one which comes nearest in meaning to the meaning of the test word. Underline the one you select.

1. to ABASE
   harm   neglect   glorify   degrade   worry

2. to MALIGN
   disgust   confuse   wound   cheat   slander

3. OVERT
   unconcealed   secret   recent   upside-down   simple

4. DEBONAIR
   passionate   angry   carefree   wealthy   young

5. INSOLVENT
   angry   rich   dirty   stingy   bankrupt

6. RESPITE
   conclusion   pause   trick   repetition   response

7. ROTUND
   plump   short   jolly   enormous   bald

8. HOVEL
   basement   crate   mansion   hut   rubbish

9. INORDINATE
   forbidden   jumbled   excessive   unexpected   insignificant

10. INTRACTABLE
    impatient   rough   fatal   hidden   stubborn

11. MANIFEST
    usual   numerous   important   apparent   strong

12. VERTIGO
    dizziness   stiffness   fever   dryness   speed

13. CONDUCIVE
    shocking   favorable   necessary   dangerous   appropriate

14. to DISCONCERT
    explain   destroy   frighten   confuse   oppose

15. to INFUSE
    fill   bother   trick   cover   expand

ABASE (ə-bAs′) v.: to degrade, humiliate, demean, humble

ABASE comes from the same Latin word as the adjective *base*, meaning *low*. To ABASE is to lower in rank or esteem, to degrade.

> "We do not feel that doing manual work ABASES us."

The word is usually used reflexively—that is, in such phrases as "ABASE myself" and "ABASE themselves."

> "The mayor refused to ABASE himself by trading insults with his opponent."
> "I think she ABASED herself by agreeing to wear that silly costume in the show."

Other forms of the word: ABASEMENT, n.

MALIGN (mə-lIn′) v.: to slander, defame

MALIGN, like *malice* and *malevolent*, comes from a Latin word meaning *bad*. To MALIGN people is to speak badly of them, particularly to lie about them maliciously.

> "The purpose of the anonymous pamphlet was to MALIGN the doctor's reputation."
> "The team's owner said he was constantly being MALIGNED by sportswriters who didn't understand what he was trying to do."

MALIGN is often used in its past participle form, MALIGNED.

> "The writer claimed that Lucrezia Borgia is one of the most falsely MALIGNED women in history; she wasn't really as bad as people say."
> "The much-MALIGNED dinosaur may actually have been a rather intelligent animal."

OVERT (O-vert′ or O′-vert) adj.: unconcealed, open, manifest

OVERT means "open to view; not concealed or hidden." The word is usually used about actions and attitudes, rather than physical objects.

> "There was plenty of secret resentment toward the boss, but no OVERT hostility."
> "The country sought an OVERT gesture of support from its allies, to show the enemy it was not alone in the struggle."
> "The governor was angered by the OVERT favoritism the newspaper showed to her opponent."

The opposite of OVERT is *covert*, which means *covered up, concealed*.

DEBONAIR (deb-ə-nair′) adj.: suave; nonchalant, carefree, lighthearted

DEBONAIR comes from a phrase in Old French, *de bon aire,* meaning "of good family or disposition." Today DEBONAIR is used about people who are suave or have a carefree, charming manner.

> "The DEBONAIR young man seemed to glide through life."
> "He longed for the DEBONAIR existence of the rich bachelor."
> "These happy, DEBONAIR people don't know what poverty and disease are like."

INSOLVENT (in-sol′-vənt) adj.: bankrupt

INSOLVENT is the combination of *solvent,* meaning "able to meet financial obligations," and the prefix *in-,* meaning *not.* Thus INSOLVENT means "unable to meet financial obligations," *bankrupt.*

> "The INSOLVENT corporation owed its employees thousands of dollars in back pay."
> "Bob told the bank he couldn't start paying off the loan because he was INSOLVENT."

Other forms of the word: INSOLVENCY, n.

RESPITE (res′pit or res′-pət) n.: a pause, rest

A RESPITE is a temporary pause from something unpleasant or distressing, an interval of rest or relief.

> "The cotton pickers worked for hours in the hot sun without RESPITE."
> "The concert was so terrible that the intermission was a welcome RESPITE."
> "Sarah looked forward to her vacation; she felt that she needed a RESPITE from her fast-paced job."

ROTUND (rO-tuhnd′) adj.: plump, rounded

ROTUND comes from a Latin word meaning *round*, and is related to English words like *rotor* and *rotate*. ROTUND is used mainly about the roundness of a person's shape. It suggests a person who is short and fat, but not excessively so.

> "He used to be skinny, but years of drinking beer have made him rather ROTUND."
> "The ROTUND man looked as though he would bounce if he fell down."

A related word, ROTUNDA, refers to a round building or a large round room.

Other forms of the word: ROTUNDITY, n.

HOVEL (huhv′-əl or hov′-əl) n.: an open shed; a hut, miserable dwelling

A HOVEL was originally an open shed used for storing tools or sheltering livestock. Now it is a hut or any small, dismal place in which people live.

> "The penniless family lived in a miserable HOVEL at the edge of town."
> "I wouldn't let a dog live in that HOVEL, much less a human being."

RUBBISH is the most common wrong answer on the Pretest, chosen by people who know that a HOVEL is something dirty and wretched, but who are unsure of its specific meaning.

INORDINATE (in-ôr′-də-nit) adj.: excessive, immoderate, exorbitant

INORDINATE comes from a Latin word meaning to *order* or *arrange,* and its root meaning is "not in order." See *in-₂* under Prefixes. The word is generally used about things that are "not in order" because they go beyond what is reasonable or acceptable.

> "Two hours is an INORDINATE amount of time to spend taking a bath."
> "Mary had an INORDINATE fondness for orange pineapple creams. She would eat them by the pound."
> "Viewers were repelled by the INORDINATE amount of violence in the movie."

INTRACTABLE (in-trak′-tə-bəl) adj.: stubborn, obstinate, unmanageable

The *tract* part of INTRACTABLE comes from a Latin word meaning to *handle* or *treat*. A person who is *tractable* is able to be handled or controlled. An INTRACTABLE person cannot be controlled, is stubborn or unmanageable. See *in-₂* under Prefixes.

> "The INTRACTABLE student simply refused to obey the teacher."
> "When it saw the trailer, the INTRACTABLE horse dug its heels into the ground and refused to move."

INTRACTABLE can also be applied to things, and means "difficult to work with" or "not easily relieved."

> "The soil was so INTRACTABLE that Mr. Brown decided to give up farming."
> "He could not mold the INTRACTABLE metal into the appropriate shape."
> "The pain was INTRACTABLE: none of the medicines seemed to help."

MANIFEST (man′-ə-fest) adj.: evident, obvious, apparent

Something that is MANIFEST is apparent either to the eye or the mind.

> "The young instructor's nervousness was so MANIFEST that everyone in the class noticed it immediately."
> "It is MANIFEST that a dog that isn't housebroken belongs outside."
> "Parking sideways across the street is a MANIFEST violation of both the law and common courtesy."

The term "MANIFEST Destiny" refers to a future event that people regard as "apparently inevitable."

> "In the 1800s, many Americans regarded territorial expansion as their nation's MANIFEST Destiny."

MANIFEST is also a verb, meaning to *show clearly.*

> "The nobleman's every action MANIFESTED his utter contempt for the common people."

Other forms of the word: MANIFESTATION, n.

VERTIGO (ver′-tə-gO) n.: dizziness

VERTIGO comes from the Latin verb *vertere*, to turn, and means *dizziness*, the feeling that the world is whirling about you. Other English words from *vertere* include *divert*, *revert*, and *convert*.

> "Just before she fainted, Jane was aware of a sensation of VERTIGO: the room seemed to start spinning around her at an increasing speed until she blacked out."

CONDUCIVE (kən-dU′-siv or kən-dyU′-siv) adj.: favorable, helpful, promoting

CONDUCIVE means *promoting, favorable.* The Latin root *duc* means *lead;* it is also found in such words as *produce* and *induce.* See *con-* under Prefixes. The adjective CONDUCIVE is always used with *to.*

> "A glass of hot milk at bedtime is often CONDUCIVE to sleep."
> "Ron found that the stress of his new job was not CONDUCIVE to domestic bliss: he yelled at his wife and children almost every evening."

DISCONCERT (dis-kən-sert′) v.: to confuse, perturb, upset

The phrase "in concert" means *in agreement, all together.* Someone who is DISCONCERTED is not "together," is confused or flustered. See *dis-* under Prefixes. The word is generally applied to people.

> "She was so DISCONCERTED by his sudden arrival that she just stood in the doorway and stared at him."
> "The noise from the stands momentarily DISCONCERTED the tennis player."
> "The rumor of possible layoffs DISCONCERTED the employees."

The adjective from DISCONCERT is DISCONCERTING. Something that is DISCONCERTING causes you to be flustered or disturbed.

> "Nancy has a DISCONCERTING way of smiling knowingly whenever anyone speaks to her."

Other forms of the word: DISCONCERTING, adj.

INFUSE (in-fyUz′) v.: to fill, instill, imbue

INFUSE comes from a Latin word meaning to *pour into.* See *in-₁* under Prefixes. The *fuse* root is also found in such words as *confuse, diffuse,* and *suffuse.* INFUSE means to *pour in* in a figurative sense, to instill or inculcate a belief, an emotion, or the like.

> "The coach INFUSED his players with a sense of pride."
> "The charges of corruption INFUSED a new spirit of bitterness into the campaign."
> "Dickens's novels are INFUSED with a delight in humanity's variety."

Other forms of the word: INFUSION, n.

Exercise 1

Answer each question with a YES or NO. Put a check in the space for YES or NO next to each question.

		Yes	No
1.	Is it pleasant to ABASE yourself?	_____	_____
2.	Would people be MALIGNED if their actions were called commendable?	_____	_____
3.	Is booing an OVERT expression of disapproval?	_____	_____
4.	Are DEBONAIR people apt to be glum?	_____	_____
5.	Do corporations seek to become INSOLVENT?	_____	_____
6.	Are RESPITES usually enjoyable?	_____	_____
7.	Are basketball players usually ROTUND?	_____	_____
8.	Would it be an ordeal to live in a HOVEL?	_____	_____
9.	Is a dollar an INORDINATE amount of money to spend on a book?	_____	_____
10.	Can a person be INTRACTABLE?	_____	_____
11.	Would someone be likely to notice a MANIFEST error?	_____	_____
12.	Could a merry-go-round cause VERTIGO?	_____	_____
13.	Is bankruptcy usually CONDUCIVE to happiness?	_____	_____
14.	Is a nervous person easily DISCONCERTED?	_____	_____
15.	Could a person be INFUSED with courage?	_____	_____

Exercise 2

Each sentence contains a test word in CAPITAL letters. Decide whether the test word is being used correctly or incorrectly in the sentence. Put a check in the space for RIGHT or WRONG next to the sentence.

		Right	Wrong
1.	The elevator quickly ABASED us to the lobby.	_____	_____
2.	The teacher MALIGNED him never to do that again.	_____	_____
3.	The spy carried out an OVERT investigation by sneaking into the embassy at night.	_____	_____
4.	George's DEBONAIR ways made him the life of every party.	_____	_____
5.	The company was declared INSOLVENT when it could no longer pay its creditors.	_____	_____
6.	The town received no RESPITE from the enemy bombing.	_____	_____
7.	Ann started exercising after someone told her she was becoming ROTUND.	_____	_____
8.	The city tore down those old HOVELS and built modern houses on the same spot.	_____	_____
9.	The miser had an INORDINATE love of gold.	_____	_____
10.	The INTRACTABLE workers agreed to do whatever their boss wanted.	_____	_____

11. The doctor's MANIFEST concern for her patients made them trust her. _____ _____

12. Standing on the roof of the building gave him such a feeling of VERTIGO that he was afraid he would fall off. _____ _____

13. Loud music in the background is not CONDUCIVE to effective studying. _____ _____

14. Charles had a DISCONCERTING habit of staring intently at complete strangers. _____ _____

15. The preacher's words INFUSED us with a desire to reform. _____ _____

Exercise 3

Each test word is followed by three other words. Decide which of the three words is LEAST CLOSELY RELATED in its meaning to the meaning of the test word. Put the letter for the word you choose in the space at the end of the line.

EXAMPLE

	TINY:	**a)** small	**b)** short	**c)** angry		C

1.	ABASE:	**a)** degrade	**b)** grovel	**c)** flinch	_____
2.	MALIGN:	**a)** delete	**b)** slander	**c)** detract	_____
3.	OVERT:	**a)** blatant	**b)** insistent	**c)** open	_____
4.	DEBONAIR:	**a)** carefree	**b)** clever	**c)** affable	_____
5.	INSOLVENT:	**a)** bankrupt	**b)** impoverished	**c)** affluent	_____
6.	RESPITE:	**a)** conclusion	**b)** recess	**c)** interval	_____
7.	ROTUND:	**a)** ruddy	**b)** portly	**c)** obese	_____
8.	HOVEL:	**a)** ranch	**b)** slum	**c)** shed	_____
9.	INORDINATE:	**a)** extraordinary	**b)** extravagant	**c)** extraneous	_____
10.	INTRACTABLE:	**a)** unruly	**b)** wanton	**c)** obstinate	_____
11.	MANIFEST:	**a)** apparent	**b)** necessary	**c)** distinct	_____
12.	VERTIGO:	**a)** hoarseness	**b)** giddiness	**c)** dizziness	_____
13.	CONDUCIVE:	**a)** contributing	**b)** helpful	**c)** simple	_____
14.	DISCONCERT:	**a)** confound	**b)** defile	**c)** nonplus	_____
15.	INFUSE:	**a)** imbue	**b)** inspire	**c)** perplex	_____

Chapter 2

Pretest

Each test word is printed in CAPITAL letters. From the five choices on the next line, select the one which comes nearest in meaning to the meaning of the test word. Underline the one you select.

1. PREDISPOSED
    inclined   unwilling   expected   too sick   discarded

2. to REPROVE
    recommend   teach   rebuke   require   shun

3. SUBTERFUGE
    escape   deception   theft   attack   hideout

4. to ACQUIESCE
    confess   obtain   insist   oppose   agree

5. ACRIMONIOUS
    formal   discouraging   bitter   friendly   noisy

6. COPIOUS
    difficult   scarce   repetitive   plentiful   grand

7. FURTIVE
    secret   dangerous   positive   unimportant   clever

8. HARBINGER
    actor   bird   forerunner   danger   historian

9. INCLEMENT
    dark   fair   changing   stormy   unusual

10. PORTENT
    copy   omen   ship   key   desire

11. ADVERSITY
    difference   luck   hardship   danger   conflict

12. to COGITATE
    disturb   lecture   remember   ponder   strain

13. CORPULENT
    wretched   merry   proud   rich   fat

14. DERISIVE
    helpful   final   mocking   unoriginal   angry

15. DISCONSOLATE
    heartbroken   excited   defeated   lonely   enraged

PREDISPOSED (prE-dis-pOzd′) adj.: inclined, tending, susceptible

One meaning of the verb to *dispose* is to *make willing*. To PREDISPOSE is to make willing in advance. See *pre-* under Prefixes. The word suggests putting someone in the right frame of mind ahead of time. It is usually used with *to*.

"His open, honest face PREDISPOSED me to believe him."

PREDISPOSE is also used about one's physical condition. In this sense it means to *make susceptible*.

"Her frail constitution PREDISPOSED her to a variety of ailments."

PREDISPOSE is more often seen in its adjectival form, PREDISPOSED. As an adjective, it generally comes after the noun it modifies.

"Because he was broke, he was PREDISPOSED to accept whatever money they offered him."

Other forms of the word: PREDISPOSE, v.
PREDISPOSITION, n.

REPROVE (ri-prUv′) v.: to rebuke, scold, admonish, reprimand

To REPROVE is to scold or criticize. The word usually suggests that the scolding is done without anger or harshness, in order to help the person.

"Sally's mother gently REPROVED her for going out without her mittens."

"The principal felt compelled to REPROVE the students for their rowdy behavior."

The noun related to REPROVE is REPROOF, which is an expression of blame or censure.

"Her mother's REPROOF made Sally decide to mend her ways."

Other forms of the word: REPROOF, n.

SUBTERFUGE (suhb′-tər-fyUj) n.: a deception, artifice, stratagem

SUBTERFUGE comes from a Latin word meaning to *flee secretly*. A SUBTERFUGE is a trick or tactic used to avoid or conceal something.

"Through various SUBTERFUGES he managed to avoid paying any income tax."

"We saw through all his SUBTERFUGES, and wouldn't let him get away with anything."

"The police used SUBTERFUGE to help the singer escape: they put a look-alike in the limousine, while the singer drove away unnoticed in a police car."

ACQUIESCE (ak-wE-es′) v.: to agree, assent, go along

To ACQUIESCE is to comply passively or tacitly. The word suggests going along with something because one is unwilling to protest or oppose it. ACQUIESCE is often followed by *in* or *to*.

"When the workers threatened to strike, management was forced to ACQUIESCE to their demand."

"I'm afraid we cannot ACQUIESCE in this matter. Our opposition is unalterable."

"He was opposed to using credit cards, but because he had no cash, he finally ACQUIESCED."

Other forms of the word: ACQUIESCENCE, n.
ACQUIESCENT, adj.

ACRIMONIOUS (ak-rə-mO′-nE-əs) adj.: bitter, stinging, sharp, biting

The Latin adjective *acer* means *sharp* or *sour*, and is found in English words like *acrid, acute, acid,* and *acerbic*. ACRIMONIOUS means *sharp* in a figurative sense, and suggests bitterness of speech, feeling, behavior, or disposition.

"Janice wrote an ACRIMONIOUS letter to her parents after they refused to come to her wedding."

"Bill could tell by her ACRIMONIOUS reply that she had a hot temper."

"She wondered whether his ACRIMONIOUS remarks about marriage stemmed from his recent divorce."

ACRIMONY is a biting sharpness or bitterness; like ACRIMONIOUS it has to do with speech, feeling, or behavior.

"The jurors never forgot the ACRIMONY with which the defendant's mother protested their verdict."

Other forms of the word: ACRIMONY, n.

COPIOUS (kO′-pE-əs) adj.: plentiful, abundant, ample

COPIOUS means *plentiful*, "existing in abundance."

"We have a COPIOUS supply of meat in the freezer."
"The composer's works are not COPIOUS, but they make up in quality what they lack in quantity."

COPIOUS is also sometimes used about language that is full of thought or wordy.

"The students were hard put to take notes on everything the professor said during his COPIOUS lecture."

FURTIVE (fer′-tiv) adj.: secret, stealthy, sneaky

FURTIVE comes from a Latin word meaning *thief*. See *-ive* under Suffixes. FURTIVE means "characterized by the stealth and watchfulness of a thief." It is applied to people, their actions, and their expressions.

"The FURTIVE soldier crept quietly through the enemy lines."
"With a FURTIVE glance around him the thief reached toward the open cash register."
"Gail signaled FURTIVELY to her brother to keep quiet about going to the movies."

HARBINGER (hahr′-bən-jər) n.: a forerunner, herald, precursor

A HARBINGER was originally a person sent ahead to prepare lodgings for English royalty when they traveled. From this, the word came to be used about anyone or anything that is a forerunner of something else.

"The sound of the trumpets was a HARBINGER of the king's arrival."
"The cold north wind is a sure HARBINGER of winter."
"The secretaries knew that the boss's early-morning frown was a HARBINGER of a bad day to come."

HARBINGER is also occasionally used as a verb.

"The poor harvest HARBINGERS a long and difficult winter for everyone."

INCLEMENT (in-klem′-ənt) adj.: stormy, severe, harsh

The word *clement* means *mild* or *merciful*. INCLEMENT is the opposite of *clement*; see *in-₂* under Prefixes. INCLEMENT means *stormy* or *severe*, and is usually used about the weather.

"The baseball game was postponed because of INCLEMENT weather."

Other forms of the word: INCLEMENCY, n.

PORTENT (pôr′tent) n.: an omen, sign, augury

A PORTENT is an omen or sign of something calamitous or very important that is about to happen.

"The natives took the eclipse to be a PORTENT of evil times to come."
"The boss's friendly smile was a PORTENT that this job would be better than Jack's previous one."

The verb related to PORTENT is PORTEND, which means "to be an omen of," to *presage*.

"These early snowstorms PORTEND a long, cold winter."

The adjective from PORTENT is PORTENTOUS, which means *ominous, fateful*. Sometimes it is used in a less threatening sense to mean *prodigious, marvelous*.

"We will always remember having lived through these PORTENTOUS times."

Other forms of the word: PORTEND, v.
PORTENTOUS, adj.

ADVERSITY (ad-ver′-sə-tE) n.: misfortune, disaster, trouble, distress

ADVERSITY is a state of misfortune or suffering.

"He kept a great deal of money in the bank as a protection against ADVERSITY."
"Susan did not let physical ADVERSITY keep her from improving her mind."
"Some artists seem to thrive on ADVERSITY; the more they suffer, the more they create."

When used in the plural, ADVERSITIES, the word means *unfortunate experiences, disasters*.

"There seemed to be no end to these ADVERSITIES; it was just one stroke of bad luck after another."

Other forms of the word: ADVERSE, adj.

COGITATE (koj'-ə-tAt) v.: to ponder, meditate, think carefully

To COGITATE is to think deeply, to consider carefully. The word does not necessarily suggest that there will be any result from the thinking.

"He smoked his pipe and COGITATED for a long time about the best place to do his fishing."
"John appeared to COGITATE for ten minutes before he answered the question."

The noun from COGITATE is COGITATION, meaning *deep thought.*

"After long COGITATION, Alan thought he had the answer."

Other forms of the word: COGITATION, n.

CORPULENT (kôr'-pyə-lənt) adj.: fat, stout, obese

CORPULENT comes from the Latin word for *body,* also the source of the English words *corpse* and *corporation.* People who are CORPULENT have too much flesh; they have large, overweight bodies. CORPULENT has a somewhat more negative sense than *fat* or *stout;* it is not quite as negative as *obese,* however, which suggests gross fatness.

"The CORPULENT passenger could barely fit into the seat on the airplane."
"Before her diet Janet was CORPULENT and unhealthy; now she is slim and feels wonderful."

Other forms of the word: CORPULENCE, n.

DERISIVE (di–rI'-siv) adj.: mocking, ridiculing, scoffing

To DERIDE is to make fun of in a bitter or contemptuous way. It comes from the Latin word for laugh, also the source of the word *ridiculous.*

"Jones said he had found a way to make himself invisible, but scientists DERIDED his claim."

DERISIVE is the adjective from DERIDE. See *-ive* under Suffixes.

"The audience responded to the stupid movie with DERISIVE laughter."
"The DERISIVE senior said that only a freshman would be dumb enough to believe that he had to go to school on Saturday."

Other forms of the word: DERIDE, v.
DERISION, n.

DISCONSOLATE (dis-kon'-sə-lit) adj.: heartbroken, dejected, depressed

To *console* means to *cheer up,* to *give comfort to.* DISCONSOLATE means "not consoled, deeply dejected, hopelessly sad." See *dis-* under Prefixes and *-ate₂* under Suffixes.

"We were DISCONSOLATE when we found out our team had been disqualified."
"Don't be DISCONSOLATE. Things are bound to get better."
"The sad expression on his face mirrored his DISCONSOLATE state of mind."

Exercise 1

Answer each question with a YES or NO. Put a check in the space for YES or NO next to each question.

		Yes	No
1.	Should a jury be PREDISPOSED to find a defendant guilty?	_____	_____
2.	Would a heroic act deserve a REPROOF?	_____	_____
3.	Would a disguise be a form of SUBTERFUGE?	_____	_____
4.	Could people ACQUIESCE in something they don't favor?	_____	_____
5.	Do ACRIMONIOUS discussions promote friendship?	_____	_____
6.	Is there a COPIOUS supply of water in the desert?	_____	_____
7.	Would a spy be FURTIVE?	_____	_____
8.	Can animals be HARBINGERS?	_____	_____
9.	Would most people enjoy having a picnic in INCLEMENT weather?	_____	_____
10.	Can a PORTENT be favorable?	_____	_____
11.	Is a depression a time of economic ADVERSITY?	_____	_____
12.	Does a sleeping person COGITATE?	_____	_____
13.	Does a CORPULENT person have a large girth?	_____	_____
14.	Might people DERIDE a buffoon?	_____	_____
15.	Would a DISCONSOLATE person need to be comforted?	_____	_____

Exercise 2

Each sentence contains a test word in CAPITAL letters. Decide whether the test word is being used correctly or incorrectly in the sentence. Put a check in the space for RIGHT or WRONG next to the sentence.

		Right	Wrong
1.	She PREDISPOSED of her Christmas presents early in December.	_____	_____
2.	Victor seemed indifferent when he was REPROVED.	_____	_____
3.	The embezzler used some very sophisticated SUBTERFUGES to escape detection.	_____	_____
4.	The company ACQUIESCED to the workers' demand for another paid holiday.	_____	_____
5.	There was considerable ACRIMONY over the unfair tactics the other team had used in the game.	_____	_____
6.	Jerry's grandmother gave him a COPIOUS serving of ice cream for dessert.	_____	_____
7.	Chuck gave a FURTIVE wink to his fellow conspirator.	_____	_____
8.	The crocus peeping up through the ground was the first HARBINGER of spring.	_____	_____
9.	The plane had difficulty landing because of the INCLEMENT weather.		

10. Everyone chose to ignore the PORTENTS of the coming war. ——— ———

11. Someday these ADVERSITIES will seem less important to us, but right now they are quite oppressive. ——— ———

12. Nancy COGITATED the right answer immediately. ——— ———

13. The CORPULENT fellow didn't need to stuff a pillow under his coat in order to play Santa Claus. ——— ———

14. The DERISIVE audience hooted the singer off the stage. ——— ———

15. Sally's parents tried to be DISCONSOLATE toward her when she lost the contest. ——— ———

Exercise 3

Each test word is followed by three other words. Decide which of the three words is LEAST CLOSELY RELATED in its meaning to the meaning of the test word. Put the letter for the word you choose in the space at the end of the line.

EXAMPLE

TINY: a) small b) short c) angry ___C___

1. PREDISPOSED: a) reminded b) susceptible c) biased ———

2. REPROVE: a) reproach b) reprimand c) repent ———

3. SUBTERFUGE: a) wile b) resistance c) trickery ———

4. ACQUIESCE: a) advise b) assent c) accede ———

5. ACRIMONIOUS: a) angry b) sinister c) sour ———

6. COPIOUS: a) lavish b) profuse c) prominent ———

7. FURTIVE: a) sinful b) secret c) cunning ———

8. HARBINGER: a) reporter b) precursor c) herald ———

9. INCLEMENT: a) harsh b) rainy c) warm ———

10. PORTENT: a) omen b) precursor c) monument ———

11. ADVERSITY: a) trouble b) misfortune c) confusion ———

12. COGITATE: a) reflect b) surprise c) meditate ———

13. CORPULENT: a) strong b) heavy c) big ———

14. DERISIVE: a) bitter b) cunning c) mocking ———

15. DISCONSOLATE: a) woeful b) dejected c) confused ———

Chapter 3

Pretest

Each test word is printed in CAPITAL letters. From the five choices on the next line, select the one which comes nearest in meaning to the meaning of the test word. Underline the one you select.

1. to EXACERBATE
   comfort   aggravate   falsify   calculate   elevate

2. FELICITY
   loyalty   ease   satisfaction   happiness   fame

3. OBLIVIOUS
   rash   helpless   high-spirited   aware   forgetful

4. SQUALOR
   cleanliness   wealth   filthiness   bitterness   storminess

5. AFFRAY
   brawl   game   party   comedy   war

6. ANTIPATHY
   depression   confusion   understanding   fear   aversion

7. ASPECT
   appearance   decision   behavior   opportunity   feeling

8. CONTRITION
   pressure   anxiety   repentance   pride   holiness

9. IMPUDENT
   helpless   cautious   shameless   courageous   playful

10. INDOLENT
    lazy   hardworking   poor   weak   mean

11. INTERLOPER
    thief   intruder   messenger   beginner   opponent

12. MILIEU
    surroundings   target   substitute   food   inhabitants

13. NEBULOUS
    false   incredible   distant   hazy   bright

14. ODIOUS
    foreign   hateful   sweet   clear   unusual

15. REPAST
    play   party   legend   beverage   meal

EXACERBATE (ig-zas'-ər-bAt) v.: to aggravate, embitter, irritate

The *acerb* part of EXACERBATE comes from a Latin word meaning *bitter* or *sour. Acerb,* or *acerbic,* also has the same meaning in English. To EXACERBATE something is to make it more bitter, to increase its severity or violence. See -ate₁ under Suffixes. The word is usually used about pain, emotions, or the like.

> "You must eat something. Going without food will only EXACERBATE your illness."
> "The mayor's thoughtless remark only served to EXACERBATE racial tensions in the city."
> "Instead of solving the problem, Jack's foolish scheme EXACERBATED it."

FELICITY (fə-lis'-ə-tE) n.: happiness, bliss; a pleasing manner

FELICITY is a rather formal term for *happiness.*

> "On their 50th anniversary, the couple were a model of wedded FELICITY."
> "At the reunion, there was such FELICITY that smiles and laughter flowed like wine."

In a less common sense, FELICITY is a pleasing manner or quality, especially in language.

> "Some say it was not the politician's platform that got him elected, but his good looks and FELICITY of speech."

Other forms of the word: FELICITOUS, adj.

OBLIVIOUS (ə-bliv'-E-əs) adj.: forgetful, unaware, unmindful

OBLIVIOUS and its related noun OBLIVION come from a Latin word meaning to *forget.* The basic meaning of OBLIVIOUS is *forgetful,* either because one chooses to forget, or because the matter is too trivial to remember. The word is usually followed by *of* or *to.*

> "The sudden new crisis made Sheila OBLIVIOUS of her previous concerns."
> "The union said it would strike if management remained OBLIVIOUS to its grievance."

Very often OBLIVIOUS is used to mean *unaware.*

> "The busy teacher was OBLIVIOUS of the talking and laughter going on all around her."

This usage is sometimes criticized as being too general and imprecise.

Other forms of the word: OBLIVION, n.

SQUALOR (skwol'-ər) n.: filthiness, corruption, baseness

The adjective SQUALID means *filthy.*

> "They lived in a SQUALID apartment, with garbage heaped everywhere."

SQUALID can also be applied to moral filth, and means *sordid.*

> "The newspaper was filled with SQUALID stories about divorce trials and ax murders."

SQUALOR is the noun from SQUALID. It too is used about both physical and moral filth.

> "Janet longs to move away from the SQUALOR of the slums."
> "The preacher denounced the moral SQUALOR in which so many people lived."

Other forms of the word: SQUALID, adj.

AFFRAY (ə-frA') n.: a brawl, noisy quarrel

In legal use, an AFFRAY is a public quarrel or fight loud enough to disturb people nearby. Generally, AFFRAY refers to any noisy or unseemly dispute.

> "What had started as a political discussion turned into such an AFFRAY that people at nearby tables got up to leave."
> "The two groups began to shout and throw garbage at each other, but the police broke up the AFFRAY."
> "The argumentative economist was always getting into bitter AFFRAYS with his equally opinionated colleagues."

14

ANTIPATHY (an-tip'-ə-thE) n.: aversion, repugnance, distaste, enmity

The *path* part of ANTIPATHY comes from a Greek word meaning *feeling;* this root is also found in *pathos, pathetic,* and *sympathy*. See *anti-* under Prefixes and *-y* under Suffixes. ANTIPATHY is a "feeling against someone or something, a sense of aversion or strong distaste. It is often followed by *to, toward,* or *against*.

> "Sam's ANTIPATHY toward his boss was so great that he finally had to quit."
> "His experience during the war left him with a strong ANTIPATHY to violence."
> "John overcame his ANTIPATHY toward cats and now owns three of them."

Other forms of the word: ANTIPATHETIC, adj.

ASPECT (as'-pekt) n.: a part or feature; trait; appearance

An ASPECT of something or someone is a part you can see with either your eyes or your mind. Its Latin root, *spectare,* meaning to *look* or *behold,* is found in words like *inspect, spectator, prospect,* and *spectacle*. An ASPECT is something that is looked at, regarded, or considered. It can mean the actual appearance of something.

> "Their painted bodies and unsmiling faces gave the natives a fierce ASPECT."
> "The combination of dusk and fog gave the forest a terrifying ASPECT."

ASPECT can also be less visual and more figurative or abstract.

> "The unfamiliar ASPECTS of Bob's new job confused him."
> "The judge instructed the jurors to consider each ASPECT of the case with the greatest care."

ASPECT also means "the manner in which something or someone is looked at or presented."

> "A salesperson tries to present his product in a favorable ASPECT."
> "I suddenly understood the poem when I regarded it in a different ASPECT."

CONTRITION (kən-trish'-ən) n.: repentance, remorse, penitence

CONTRITION and its adjective CONTRITE come from a Latin word meaning to *bruise* or *grind,* also the source of the words *attrition* and *detritus*. People who are CONTRITE are bruised or broken in spirit because of sorrow for their sins. CONTRITION is sincere regret and sorrow for having done wrong.

> "The child showed no CONTRITION for having stolen the money. In fact, he appeared to be happy that he had done it."
> "We could tell Jane's CONTRITION for her crime was real: she couldn't stop crying as she tried to say how sorry she was."
> "The criminal's words of CONTRITION did not sway the judge."

Other forms of the word: CONTRITE, adj.

IMPUDENT (im'-pyU-dənt) adj.: shameless, disrespectful, impertinent, brazen

IMPUDENT is made up of the prefix *im-,* meaning *not,* and the root *pud,* from a Latin word meaning to *feel shame*. An IMPUDENT person is shameless, especially in his or her attitude toward others. The word often stresses boldness and lack of respect.

> "The IMPUDENT student simply ignored the principal when she spoke to him."
> "The boss fired the worker because of his IMPUDENT behavior."

The noun from IMPUDENT is IMPUDENCE.

> "Jane's mother made her apologize for her IMPUDENCE toward the guests."
> "Because of his constant IMPUDENCE, Paul was told that he was no longer welcome as a member of the business association."

Other forms of the word: IMPUDENCE, n.

INDOLENT (in'-də-lənt) adj.: lazy, slothful

INDOLENT means "habitually lazy." An INDOLENT person is not inclined to work or to perform any other kind of exertion.

> "She is so INDOLENT that she spends the entire summer lying on the beach."
> "The INDOLENT fellows hung around the park all day, playing cards and watching the cars go by."

The noun form of INDOLENT is INDOLENCE.

> "The boss accused his workers of INDOLENCE, saying that all they wanted to do was take long lunch hours."

Other forms of the word: INDOLENCE, n.

INTERLOPER (in'-tər-lOp-ər) n.: an intruder, trespasser

An INTERLOPER is an intruder, someone who interferes in other people's affairs, often in order to gain a privilege or a right that belongs to someone else.

> "A group of INTERLOPERS appeared and tried to take over our mining claims."
> "She said no one had invited Dave to the party; he was nothing but an INTERLOPER."

The verb form is INTERLOPE, to *intrude, meddle, butt in.*

> "The company official accused the government of constantly INTERLOPING in the affairs of business."

Other forms of the word: INTERLOPE, v.

MILIEU (mEl-yər') n.: surroundings, environment, setting

Note the pronunciation. MILIEU is a French word, and has retained its French pronunciation. The MILIEU of people is their surroundings, the social and physical setting in which they live.

> "The book examines the cultural MILIEU in Vienna at the turn of the century."
> "She came out of the slums of New York City—and anyone who has lived in that MILIEU knows the obstacles she had to overcome."
> "The painter did his best work in a strange MILIEU of poets, out-of-work actors, and assorted eccentrics."

NEBULOUS (neb'-yə-ləs) adj.: hazy, cloudy, indistinct, vague

NEBULOUS comes from the Latin word for *cloud.* See *-ous* under Suffixes. Something that is NEBULOUS is hazy and indistinct, like a cloud. The word is often used in an extended sense about anything that is dimly realized or not clearly established.

> "The boundary between the countries is quite NEBULOUS; no one is sure where one country ends and the other begins."
> "Their plans for the party are still NEBULOUS, but I'm sure everything will be settled by next week."
> "NEBULOUS memories and ideas floated through her mind as she lay on the hammock."

Other forms of the word: NEBULOSITY, n.

ODIOUS (O'-dE-əs) adj.: hateful, abhorrent, offensive, detestable

ODIOUS and the noun ODIUM come from a Latin word meaning to *hate.* Something that is ODIOUS arouses one's hatred or disgust.

> "I cannot tell you how shocked I am by your ODIOUS conduct."
> "Finally they abolished their ODIOUS policy of excluding women from their club."
> "The ODIOUS band of criminals would stop at nothing in carrying out their fiendish plans."

Other forms of the word: ODIUM, n.

REPAST (ri-past' or rE'-past) n.: a meal, food

A REPAST is a meal, or the food provided at a meal.

> "This salad will make a pleasant summer REPAST."
> "For our evening REPAST we will have chicken wings and asparagus."

The *past* part of REPAST leads many people to pick *legend* on the Pretest as the word's meaning. The derivation of REPAST has nothing to do with time, however.

Exercise 1

Answer each question with a YES or NO. Put a check in the space for YES or NO next to each question.

		Yes	No
1.	Could cigarette smoking EXACERBATE a respiratory infection?	_____	_____
2.	Does living in a hovel cause FELICITY?	_____	_____
3.	Is it possible to be OBLIVIOUS of noisy surroundings?	_____	_____
4.	Is a palace likely to be SQUALID?	_____	_____
5.	Could an AFFRAY involve bitter words?	_____	_____
6.	Do mothers usually show ANTIPATHY toward their children?	_____	_____
7.	Are there furtive ASPECTS to being an undercover agent?	_____	_____
8.	Would a CONTRITE person be likely to apologize?	_____	_____
9.	Would a teacher want to rebuke a pupil for IMPUDENCE?	_____	_____
10.	Would an INDOLENT person make a good employee?	_____	_____
11.	Are INTERLOPERS welcome?	_____	_____
12.	Can people be part of a MILIEU?	_____	_____
13.	Can a thought be NEBULOUS?	_____	_____
14.	Is it ODIOUS to be a murderer?	_____	_____
15.	Could a banquet be a REPAST?	_____	_____

Exercise 2

Each sentence contains a test word in CAPITAL letters. Decide whether the test word is being used correctly or incorrectly in the sentence. Put a check in the space for RIGHT or WRONG next to the sentence.

		Right	Wrong
1.	The teacher EXACERBATED them for smoking on the school grounds.	_____	_____
2.	Mr. Jones claimed that nothing was more important to him than his wife's FELICITY.	_____	_____
3.	When hard at work, John became OBLIVIOUS of his surroundings.	_____	_____
4.	The SQUALOR of the teenagers' bedrooms contrasted vividly with the cleanliness of the rest of the house.	_____	_____
5.	It was a quiet AFFRAY, attended only by his close friends.	_____	_____
6.	I have considerable ANTIPATHY for your predicament; unfortunately, there is nothing I can do to help you.	_____	_____
7.	Looking at it from a different ASPECT, I can understand why she was upset.	_____	_____
8.	The murderer expressed great CONTRITION when she said the victim got what he deserved.	_____	_____

9. The IMPUDENT children stuck their tongues out at the woman. _____ _____

10. His INDOLENCE is astonishing; he wouldn't get out of bed if he didn't have to eat. _____ _____

11. Betty called the new salesman an INTERLOPER for trying to take over some of her accounts. _____ _____

12. The refined lady seemed out of place in the rough-and-tumble MILIEU of the waterfront. _____ _____

13. They painted their house a bright, NEBULOUS color. _____ _____

14. She exclaimed with delight at the ODIOUS smell of the roses. _____ _____

15. The man entertained us with REPASTS of things that had happened long ago. _____ _____

Exercise 3

Each test word is followed by three other words. Decide which of the three words is LEAST CLOSELY RELATED in its meaning to the meaning of the test word. Put the letter for the word you choose in the space at the end of the line.

EXAMPLE

TINY:	a) small	b) short	c) angry	C
1. EXACERBATE:	a) worsen	b) destroy	c) embitter	_____
2. FELICITY:	a) pleasure	b) contentment	c) nostalgia	_____
3. OBLIVIOUS:	a) unaware	b) careful	c) forgetful	_____
4. SQUALOR:	a) filth	b) sordidness	c) danger	_____
5. AFFRAY:	a) meeting	b) quarrel	c) wrangle	_____
6. ANTIPATHY:	a) ferocity	b) repugnance	c) aversion	_____
7. ASPECT:	a) belief	b) view	c) trait	_____
8. CONTRITION:	a) regret	b) remorse	c) resentment	_____
9. IMPUDENT:	a) angry	b) brash	c) insolent	_____
10. INDOLENT:	a) lonely	b) lethargic	c) languid	_____
11. INTERLOPER:	a) conqueror	b) meddler	c) intruder	_____
12. MILIEU:	a) discipline	b) atmosphere	c) background	_____
13. NEBULOUS:	a) unclear	b) unknown	c) imprecise	_____
14. ODIOUS:	a) hateful	b) disgusting	c) fearful	_____
15. REPAST:	a) dessert	b) breakfast	c) water	_____

Review Test 1—Chapters 1–3

Fill in each blank with the test word (or a form of the test word) which best fits the sentence. Use the words listed below.

ACQUIESCE	CONDUCIVE	FELICITY	INDOLENT	OVERT
ACRIMONIOUS	COPIOUS	FURTIVE	INFUSE	REPAST
ADVERSITY	DEBONAIR	HARBINGER	INORDINATE	ROTUND
AFFRAY	EXACERBATE	HOVEL	MALIGN	SUBTERFUGE
ANTIPATHY				

1. The noisy _____ between the two gangs awoke everyone in the neighborhood.

2. To avoid publicity, the movie star adopted such _____ as registering in hotels under an assumed name.

3. The arrival of flocks of birds from the south was a(n) _____ of spring.

4. He was a totally honest man, and felt a strong _____ toward those who didn't tell the truth.

5. The _____ thief moved stealthily through the darkened warehouse.

6. Many studies have shown that physical exercise is _____ to good health.

7. We had a delightful _____ at the fine French restaurant.

8. Despite these temporary _____, he was ultimately able to triumph.

9. The _____ dispute over who would pay the bill threatened to turn into a full-scale fight.

10. Everyone admired the _____ youth's lighthearted ways.

11. The children grew up in a wretched _____ without running water or electricity.

12. The _____ woman spent all her time watching television instead of working.

13. Far from easing the pain, this new drug seems to _____ it.

14. The teacher frowned and shook her head and made other _____ signs of her displeasure.

15. We felt that a week was a(n) _____ amount of time to wait for our telephone to be fixed.

16. Harry could always get a job playing Santa Claus because of his _____ shape.

17. Mary puts _____ amounts of catsup on everything she eats.

18. The mayor's enemies _____ him by spreading the false rumor that he had taken a bribe.

19. The sight of our old home _____ us with a profound sense of nostalgia.

20. With a loving husband and an exciting job she thought nothing could disturb her _____; then tragedy struck.

21. We insisted that he go along with us on this, but he refused to _____ to our demand.

Fill in each blank with the test word (or a form of the test word) which best fits the sentence. Use the words listed below.

ABASE	DERISIVE	INSOLVENT	NEBULOUS	REPROVE
ASPECT	DISCONCERT	INTERLOPER	OBLIVIOUS	RESPITE
COGITATE	DISCONSOLATE	INTRACTABLE	ODIOUS	SQUALOR
CONTRITION	IMPUDENT	MANIFEST	PORTENT	VERTIGO
CORPULENT	INCLEMENT	MILIEU	PREDISPOSED	

22. The writer lived in the exotic _____ of the jungles of Sri Lanka.

23. I'm afraid the weather is going to be _____; a severe storm is headed our way.

24. The high priest said the appearance of the comet was a(n) _____ of some great calamity.

25. Al was momentarily _____ by the unexpected sound of laughter, but then he realized it was only the television.

26. The business recession caused many companies to become _____.

27. The audience's displeasure with the performance was so _____ that even the stagehands noticed it.

28. The _____ child told the teacher she was stupid.

29. The _____ owners refused to meet any of the players' demands.

30. If you continue to gain weight, you won't be just heavy, you'll be _____.

31. Andrea was absolutely _____ when she lost the competition; nothing we said could cheer her up.

32. Their plans were rather _____ at first, but they became clearer as time went by.

33. When he was angry, his expression took on a fierce _____.

34. The criminal expressed no _____ for his evil deed; in fact, he said he'd do it again.

35. Since Alan's brothers had been smart, the teacher was _____ to believe that he was smart too.

36. The incredible _____ of the abandoned house defeated our efforts to clean it up.

37. Sarah was completely _____ to all of the petty little problems of everyday life.

38. Being alone in an open space gave her a feeling of _____; the world would seem to spin around her, and she'd almost lose her balance.

39. Simpson had to _____ a long time about the difficult problem he needed to solve.

40. I'm no _____; I have as much right to be here as you do.

41. The _____ girls laughed scornfully at his feeble attempt to jump rope.

42. The judge gave the man the maximum sentence, calling his crime _____ and an offense to all decent citizens.

43. After two hours of earsplitting noise we received a welcome _____ when the man operating the jackhammer went to lunch.

44. The professor _____ Tom for not getting his paper in on time, but said it wouldn't affect his grade.

45. Jim was willing to _____ himself by begging for money from his relatives.

Chapter 4

Pretest

Each test word is printed in CAPITAL letters. From the five choices on the next line, select the one which comes nearest in meaning to the meaning of the test word. Underline the one you select.

1. to ASCRIBE
    propose   attribute   consider   command   write
2. AUSPICIOUS
    strange   unfortunate   curious   favorable   cautious
3. to GLOWER
    scowl   groan   beam   shrink   cry
4. GUILE
    evil   trickiness   innocence   energy   sorrow
5. OBDURATE
    stubborn   inferior   powerful   mistaken   angry
6. PARITY
    precision   normality   completeness   equality   humor
7. PAUCITY
    variety   truthfulness   capacity   abundance   scarcity
8. to TRANSGRESS
    obey   violate   carry   advance   disagree
9. TRAVAIL
    toil   triumph   secrecy   danger   hostility
10. WAN
    secret   tiny   sickly   old   nice
11. to COMMISERATE
    agree   discuss   assist   suffer   sympathize
12. to DISCERN
    learn   notice   forget   remove   expect
13. PONDEROUS
    stupid   broad   dangerous   heavy   gloomy
14. SHIFTLESS
    lazy   busy   silent   evil   hungry
15. AMITY
    friendship   hostility   dullness   fairness   cheerfulness

ASCRIBE (ə-skrIb') v.: to attribute

To ASCRIBE something is to attribute or assign it as a cause or source. The word comes from the Latin *scribere,* to *write,* and originally meant "to add to a writing or enter in a list." This Latin source is found in words like *prescribe* and *scribe.* Sometimes ASCRIBE still carries with it the sense of writing, in that it suggests the knowledge or authority of an expert. But ASCRIBE is often used interchangeably with the verb *attribute.* It is usually used with *to.*

"After careful examination, the scholar ASCRIBED the newly discovered diary to the second mate of the famous admiral."

"He ASCRIBES his financial misfortunes to careless bookkeeping."

Other forms of the word: ASCRIPTION, n.

AUSPICIOUS (ô-spish'-əs) adj.: favorable, propitious, fortunate

AUSPICIOUS comes from Latin words meaning "to look at birds," and refers to the ancient Roman practice of telling the future by observing the flight of birds. Something that is AUSPICIOUS is a good omen; it augurs well for the future, usually because it is successful or fortunate itself.

"The singer's debut was AUSPICIOUS; the critics said she had a great career ahead of her."

"The first day of school was AUSPICIOUS; everything seemed to go well for Dale."

"The day began AUSPICIOUSLY when Bill found a five-dollar bill on the sidewalk."

GLOWER (glow'-ər) v.: to scowl, frown

To GLOWER is to stare blackly, to look with sullen anger. It is usually followed by *at.*

"The professor GLOWERED at the student who dared to criticize his lecture."

"The customer GLOWERED at the clerk and demanded his money back."

Beam is the most common wrong answer on the Pretest, probably because of the *glow* part of GLOWER. GLOWER is not related to the word *glow,* however. Notice that its pronunciation is different: GLOWER rhymes with *shower.*

GUILE (gIl) n.: trickery, treachery, craftiness, duplicity

GUILE is treacherous cunning, the use of one's cleverness in order to deceive.

"He used GUILE and deceit to worm his way into the king's circle of advisors."

"James is entirely without GUILE. He has never tried to trick or cheat anyone in his life."

Evil is frequently chosen as the synonym for GUILE by people who know that GUILE is a bad quality, but aren't sure of its exact meaning.

Other forms of the word: GUILEFUL, adj.
GUILELESS, adj.

OBDURATE (ob'-dyU-rət or ob'-dU-rət) adj.: stubborn, inflexible, unyielding, intractable

OBDURATE comes from the Latin word for *hard,* also the source for the word *durable.* Someone who is OBDURATE is hardened against any influence, especially appeals to reform or to be merciful.

"We begged the teacher to let us out of class early, but she was OBDURATE."

"The OBDURATE criminal said he would never give up his life of crime."

Other forms of the word: OBDURACY, n.

PARITY (par'-ə-tE) n.: equality, equivalence, correspondence

PARITY comes from a Latin word meaning *equal,* also the source of the English words *par* and *compare.* PARITY means *equality.* It is usually used in a technical sense about exact equivalence of value or amount, while the word *equality* often stresses the sense of equal rights. For example, PARITY is the equivalent in value of a sum of money as expressed in a different currency.

"The new soccer league's aim was to achieve PARITY with the older league."

"There was a lack of PARITY in the pay scales at the company: some people were paid a lot less than others for doing exactly the same kind of work."

PAUCITY (pô'-sə-tE) n.: scarcity, dearth, fewness

PAUCITY is smallness of number or amount, *scarcity, scantiness.*

> "There was a PAUCITY of good actors at the tryout for the school play."
> "The PAUCITY of available funds will make it very difficult for us to complete the project on time."
> "There was no PAUCITY of advice for Joe about how to solve the problem, but finally he had to decide for himself."

TRANSGRESS (trans-gres') v.: to go beyond a limit; to violate, break

TRANSGRESS comes from a Latin word meaning *go beyond* or *step across.* See *trans-* under Prefixes. The *gress* root is also found in words like *progress, regress,* and *egress.* TRANSGRESS is usually used in a figurative sense, of going beyond some legal or moral limit.

> "He admitted he had TRANSGRESSED the law, and was willing to take his punishment."

The word is often used without a direct object, in which case it means to *sin* or *trespass.*

> "According to her religion, she TRANSGRESSED whenever she drank coffee or liquor."

The noun is TRANSGRESSION, which means a *violation* or *breach.*

> "He knew that we would never forgive his countless TRANSGRESSIONS."

TRANSGRESS is occasionally used about physically going beyond a limit or boundary, and this might suggest *advance* as a synonym on the Pretest.

Other forms of the word: TRANSGRESSION, n.

TRAVAIL (trə-vAl' or trav'-Al) n.: toil, labor; suffering, anguish

TRAVAIL is hard work, especially when accompanied by pain or suffering. It comes from a Latin word for a torture device.

> "It must have taken years of TRAVAIL to build the pyramids."

Sometimes the emphasis is so strongly on the suffering that this becomes more important to the word's meaning than the labor.

> "He recounted his family's TRAVAILS during the long and dangerous trip across the plains."

The most popular wrong answer on the Pretest is *triumph,* possibly because of a confusion of TRAVAIL with *prevail.*

WAN (won) adj.: sickly, pale, pallid

WAN means "lacking color or vitality." The word often suggests that this paleness is the result of sickness; these two ideas are of about equal importance to the word's meaning.

> "After her long illness Sheila looked WAN and haggard."
> "The child gave a WAN smile and said he was feeling a little better."

COMMISERATE (kə-miz'-ə-rAt) v.: to sympathize, condole

See *com-* under Prefixes and *-ate₁* under Suffixes. The *miser* part of COMMISERATE comes from the same Latin root as *misery* and *miserable.* To COMMISERATE with people is literally to feel miserable along with them. The word is applied to a feeling of sympathy or pity, especially when it is spoken or expressed publicly. It is usually followed by *with.*

> "The police officer COMMISERATED with us over the loss of our valuables, but said there was nothing he could do."
> "I can't really COMMISERATE with him because I don't know why he's so unhappy."
> "He COMMISERATED with me about my problems, but he could do nothing to help me solve them."

Other forms of the word: COMMISERATION, n.

DISCERN (di-sərn′ or di-zərn′) v.: to notice, perceive, detect, distinguish

DISCERN comes from a Latin word meaning "to sift apart." See *dis-* under Prefixes. DISCERN can be used about sight, and means to *make out* or *notice*, especially something that is far away or hard to see.

"We could barely DISCERN the ship's sails in the distance."

DISCERN is also used about the other senses.

"I could not DISCERN a great deal of difference between the two recordings of the piece."

And it is used about recognizing or distinguishing something mentally.

"She DISCERNED that it would be difficult to get ahead in the company without more education."

"I couldn't DISCERN any sympathy in her attitude."

Other forms of the word: DISCERNIBLE, adj.
DISCERNING, adj.
DISCERNMENT, n.

PONDEROUS (pon′-də-rəs) adj.: heavy, massive, cumbersome; oppressive, dull

PONDEROUS comes from a Latin word meaning *weight;* it is related to the English word *pound.* The basic meaning of PONDEROUS is "having great weight," *heavy.* The word especially emphasizes the clumsiness that results from this weight.

"The PONDEROUS old dictionary was so heavy the child could barely lift it from the shelf."

In an extended sense, PONDEROUS is used about anything that is heavy for the mind or spirit; in this sense the word means *labored, dull.*

"The after-dinner speaker gave a long and PONDEROUS talk on the history of the Soviet Union's fiscal policy."

On the Pretest, many people chose *gloomy* as the meaning of PONDEROUS, probably through a vague understanding of this extended sense of PONDEROUS.

SHIFTLESS (shift′-ləs) adj.: lazy, idle, lacking ambition

An old meaning of the word *shift* is *resourcefulness.* This sense can still be seen in the adjective *shifty,* which means *resourceful* in a bad sense, *tricky, cunning.* Someone who is SHIFTLESS lacks resourcefulness. See *-less* under Suffixes. The word nowadays also emphasizes lack of ambition or energy.

"Dave is a SHIFTLESS fellow who will never amount to anything."

"The bar was filled with SHIFTLESS men who had nothing better to do than drink all day."

The most common wrong answer is *evil,* probably chosen by people who know that it is bad to be SHIFTLESS, but aren't quite sure why.

AMITY (am′-ə-tE) n.: friendship, peaceful relations

AMITY comes from a Latin word meaning *friend,* also the source of *amiable* and *amicable.* See *-y* under Suffixes. AMITY is *friendship,* especially between nations. The word often suggests that two people or groups get along despite at least potential sources of discord.

"The settlers and the natives lived together in comparative AMITY for several years."

"The lack of AMITY among the South American countries provided a constant threat of war in the hemisphere."

"They appeared to live in AMITY, but deep down they really disliked each other."

Exercise 1

Answer each question with a YES or NO. Put a check in the space for YES or NO next to each question.

		Yes	No
1.	Can filthiness sometimes be ASCRIBED to laziness?	_____	_____
2.	Would a fumble on the first play be an AUSPICIOUS start for a football team?	_____	_____
3.	Would a friendly person frequently GLOWER?	_____	_____
4.	Would most people consider GUILE to be offensive?	_____	_____
5.	Do OBDURATE people change their minds easily?	_____	_____
6.	Would an underpaid worker want to achieve PARITY with other workers?	_____	_____
7.	Would a PAUCITY of money make it difficult to pay bills?	_____	_____
8.	Would most people usually feel guilty about committing a TRANSGRESSION?	_____	_____
9.	Does TRAVAIL cause happiness?	_____	_____
10.	Is Santa Claus usually pictured as being WAN?	_____	_____
11.	Is a self-centered person likely to COMMISERATE with others?	_____	_____
12.	Can colors and shapes be DISCERNED?	_____	_____
13.	Is a comedy supposed to be PONDEROUS?	_____	_____
14.	Are business executives generally SHIFTLESS?	_____	_____
15.	Does hatred contribute to AMITY?	_____	_____

Exercise 2

Each sentence contains a test word in CAPITAL letters. Decide whether the test word is being used correctly or incorrectly in the sentence. Put a check in the space for RIGHT or WRONG next to the sentence.

		Right	Wrong
1.	Bill ASCRIBED them that all was well and that he'd be home soon.	_____	_____
2.	Don't be AUSPICIOUS; the work will get done on time.	_____	_____
3.	The teacher GLOWERED at the student who came to class late.	_____	_____
4.	The Greeks couldn't conquer Troy by force, so they decided to use GUILE.	_____	_____
5.	Mary Ann OBDURATELY refused to listen to our arguments.	_____	_____
6.	Johnson claimed there was a lack of PARITY in the agreement: he was giving up much more than he was getting.	_____	_____
7.	There is no PAUCITY that we can go with you on Saturday. We're just too busy.	_____	_____
8.	The explorers TRANSGRESSED rapidly through the woods.	_____	_____
9.	The victorious general sent word of his TRAVAIL over the enemy.	_____	_____
10.	The WAN face of the spurned lover showed how much he was suffering.	_____	_____

25

11. The teacher COMMISERATED her students by giving them so much home-work.   _____   _____

12. Bill's parents DISCERNED a subtle change in him when he came back from summer camp.   _____   _____

13. The book's theme seemed interesting, but the author's treatment of it was rather PONDEROUS.   _____   _____

14. These SHIFTLESS teenagers dropped out of school and just hang around the park all day.   _____   _____

15. The AMITY between the two nations was shattered by the dispute over who owned the tiny island.   _____   _____

Exercise 3

Each test word is followed by three other words. Decide which of the three words is LEAST CLOSELY RELATED in its meaning to the meaning of the test word. Put the letter for the word you choose in the space at the end of the line.

EXAMPLE

	TINY:	**a)** small	**b)** short	**c)** angry	__C__
1.	ASCRIBE:	**a)** assign	**b)** impute	**c)** transfer	_____
2.	AUSPICIOUS:	**a)** encouraging	**b)** fearful	**c)** favorable	_____
3.	GLOWER:	**a)** stare	**b)** blare	**c)** glare	_____
4.	GUILE:	**a)** sincerity	**b)** cleverness	**c)** deception	_____
5.	OBDURATE:	**a)** unyielding	**b)** unmerciful	**c)** unpopular	_____
6.	PARITY:	**a)** mercy	**b)** fairness	**c)** equivalence	_____
7.	PAUCITY:	**a)** scarcity	**b)** glut	**c)** want	_____
8.	TRANSGRESS:	**a)** misbehave	**b)** sin	**c)** travel	_____
9.	TRAVAIL:	**a)** ordeal	**b)** suffering	**c)** exercise	_____
10.	WAN:	**a)** pallid	**b)** unhealthy	**c)** feverish	_____
11.	COMMISERATE:	**a)** understand	**b)** empathize	**c)** wish	_____
12.	DISCERN:	**a)** observe	**b)** expect	**c)** detect	_____
13.	PONDEROUS:	**a)** massive	**b)** tumultuous	**c)** laborious	_____
14.	SHIFTLESS:	**a)** recreational	**b)** lazy	**c)** slothful	_____
15.	AMITY:	**a)** neighborliness	**b)** peace	**c)** distance	_____

Chapter 5

Pretest

Each test word is printed in CAPITAL letters. From the five choices on the next line, select the one which comes nearest in meaning to the meaning of the test word. Underline the one you select.

1. GERMANE
   foreign   sickening   relevant   logical   crucial
2. GIBE
   compliment   jeer   punch   riddle   lie
3. INIMITABLE
   matchless   unchanging   frequent   threatening   unbeaten
4. ITINERANT
   unpredictable   occasional   begging   selling   journeying
5. MELLIFLUOUS
   bitter tasting   soft   convincing   grating   sweet-sounding
6. PUGNACIOUS
   greedy   ugly   quarrelsome   unhappy   strong
7. AFICIONADO
   enthusiast   ruler   criminal   rancher   champion
8. to CEDE
   examine   start   accept   give up   turn down
9. to DEBASE
   destroy   corrupt   improve   move   forget
10. to FOMENT
    complete   stir up   uncover   talk about   advise
11. FORBEARANCE
    confidence   faith   respect   patience   excitement
12. JOCOSE
    sullen   plump   humorous   drunken   insulting
13. to VEX
    trick   scorn   confuse   comfort   annoy
14. to BURGEON
    rot   develop   shine   float   breathe
15. to DISTEND
    swell   shrink   warp   deface   postpone

GERMANE (jər-mAn') adj.: relevant, pertinent, related

GERMANE comes from an obsolete English word meaning "having the same parents." GERMANE means "closely related" in a figurative sense, to a subject or an occasion, for example. It is usually followed by *to*.

"The chairman felt that Jennifer's point was not GERMANE to the discussion."

"His stories were amusing, but also quite GERMANE to the serious issue about which he was speaking."

"These speculations are interesting but not GERMANE; they should be deleted from the book."

GIBE (jIb) v.: to jeer, taunt, mock, ridicule

GIBE is also sometimes spelled JIBE.

To GIBE is to taunt, to make mocking remarks. The remarks can be good-natured, but more often they are sarcastic, intending to hurt. GIBE is often followed by *at*.

"The other boys GIBED at Peter for walking Cindy home, but secretly they were jealous."

"The newspapers GIBED the owner of the baseball team for his ridiculous antics."

GIBE is also a noun, meaning "a taunting remark."

"Helen paid no attention to the GIBES and insults of her classmates when she started taking lessons on the tuba."

INIMITABLE (in-im'-ə-tə-bəl) adj.: matchless, unique

INIMITABLE is made up of the prefix *in-*, meaning *not*, the suffix *-able*, and the root *imit*, also found in the word *imitate*. Something that is INIMITABLE is not able to be imitated, usually because it is so good.

"We begged Danny to do his INIMITABLE impression of Frank Sinatra."

"Bill told the story of his first day at college in his own INIMITABLE style."

"The INIMITABLE Vincent van Gogh created some of the greatest paintings of the nineteenth century."

ITINERANT (I-tin'-ə-rənt) adj.: journeying, traveling, nomadic, peripatetic

ITINERANT comes from a Latin word meaning *journey*, also the source of the word ITINERARY, which is a record or route of a journey. ITINERANT means "moving from place to place." It is especially applied to people whose work entails a great deal of traveling.

"The ITINERANT actors would put on a play in any town where they could rent a hall."

"The ITINERANT preacher gave a sermon in a different church every Sunday."

"He loved the ITINERANT life; nothing could persuade him to settle down."

MELLIFLUOUS (mə-lif'-lU-əs) adj.: sweet-sounding, honeyed, smoothly flowing

The *melli-* part of MELLIFLUOUS comes from the Latin word for *honey*. The *flu* part is the Latin root meaning *flow*, also found in *fluent*. See *-ous* under Suffixes. MELLIFLUOUS literally means "flowing with honey." Although the word is occasionally used with this literal meaning, it usually has the figurative meaning of "flowing sweetly or smoothly," and is applied to sounds, voices, or the like.

"The singer's MELLIFLUOUS voice enchanted the audience."

"The baby fell asleep to the MELLIFLUOUS sounds of the lullaby."

PUGNACIOUS (pəg-nA'-shəs) adj.: quarrelsome, belligerent, aggressive, truculent, combative

PUGNACIOUS comes from a Latin word meaning *fight*, which in turn comes from a word meaning *fist*. This word is also the source of *pugilism*, which is a formal term for boxing. PUGNACIOUS means "eager to fight," and is usually used about a person who is naturally or characteristically given to fighting.

"The PUGNACIOUS sailors liked nothing better than to get into a brawl when they went ashore."

"He was quite PUGNACIOUS when it came to defending the reputation of his school."

"Sandra's PUGNACIOUS manner made it very difficult for us to work with her."

Other forms of the word: PUGNACITY, n.

AFICIONADO (ə-fE-sE-ə-na′-dO) n.: an ardent devotee, enthusiast, zealot

AFICIONADO comes directly from Spanish and literally means "one who is affectionate." But in English its sense is much stronger than "affectionate." It means "one who is ardently devoted to or enthusiastic about something."

> "The bullfighting AFICIONADOS cheered the toreador with great fervor."
> "The rare first edition of her poems was prized by collectors and cherished by her AFICIONADOS."
> "My professor insisted that I could never consider myself a true AFICIONADO of Shakespeare until I had made a pilgrimage to Stratford."

CEDE (sEd) v.: to give up, grant, relinquish

To CEDE something is to relinquish the possession of it, especially in a formal manner, through a treaty or other official act. It is usually used about rights or territory.

> "Under the terms of the treaty, the United States CEDED the land to Canada."
> "The judge ruled that the company had to CEDE all rights in the invention to its competitor."

DEBASE (di-bAs′) v.: to corrupt, degrade, adulterate, vitiate

DEBASE is related to the adjective *base,* meaning *low* or *inferior.* To DEBASE something is to lower its value or quality.

> "The so-called 'modern adaptation' DEBASES Shakespeare's play by omitting all the great poetry."
> "I said I would not DEBASE myself by appearing on the same program with my opponent."

Virtually everyone who takes the Pretest knows that DEBASE means something bad, but many think it means *destroy* rather than *corrupt.* DEBASE is not quite that strong. To DEBASE is to lower the quality of, not to destroy.

Other forms of the word: DEBASEMENT, n.

FOMENT (fO-ment′) v.: to stir up, instigate, incite, rouse

FOMENT is usually used about rebellions and other violent actions. It means to *stir up,* "to promote the growth of." The word suggests a persistent goading or incitement for a bad purpose.

> "The mayor said that outside agitators were responsible for FOMENTING the riots in his city."
> "She FOMENTED trouble in the organization by spreading rumors and telling lies."
> "The president accused the Communists of FOMENTING revolution in the South American country."

FORBEARANCE (fôr-bair′-əns) n.: patience, restraint

To FORBEAR from doing something is to refrain from doing it, especially when it is your right. FORBEARANCE is the noun from FORBEAR. People who show FORBEARANCE are patient and restrained; they hold back from exacting punishment, criticizing someone, or demanding their rights.

> "I thought she showed remarkable FORBEARANCE in putting up with her husband's drinking all these years."
> "The bank's FORBEARANCE finally ended when he fell six months behind in his loan payments."

Other forms of the word: FORBEAR, v.

JOCOSE (jO-kOs′) adj.: humorous, playful, merry

JOCOSE is related to the words *joke* and *jocular;* all come from a Latin word meaning *jest* or *joke.* JOCOSE means "characterized by joking," *humorous, waggish.*

> "Bill is the life of every party; with his JOCOSE disposition, he keeps everybody in stitches."
> "Brenda resented Dan's JOCOSE remarks about her weight, even though he thought he was very funny."
> "When Sue complained that she didn't want to go to school, her father JOCOSELY suggested that she quit and become a trapeze artist."

Other forms of the word: JOCOSITY, n.

VEX (veks) v.: to irritate, annoy, bother; to puzzle, perplex, baffle

To VEX is to annoy or irritate, often with small matters, but usually to the point of real frustration or anger.

> "Joe's wife was so VEXED by his behavior that she refused to speak to him for a week."
> "The employees' constant lateness VEXED the boss."

In a slightly different sense VEX means *baffle* or *perplex*. The word suggests irritation and annoyance in this sense as well.

> "George was VEXED by the problem of how to make ends meet on his salary."

The adjective from VEX is VEXATIOUS; it means "causing someone to be VEXED," *annoying*.

> "False alarms are not just VEXATIOUS to fire departments, they are hazardous."

Other forms of the word: VEXATION, n.
VEXATIOUS, adj.

BURGEON (ber'-jən) v.: to develop, flourish, sprout

To BURGEON is to sprout or grow like a budding flower. BURGEON usually emphasizes new and rapid growth, like that of a flower in springtime.

> "With the new piano teacher, Alan's talent suddenly started to BURGEON."
> "Over the summer vacation their mild affection for each other BURGEONED into love."
> "The two principals tried to end the BURGEONING rivalry between their schools."

DISTEND (dis-tend') v.: to swell, expand, bloat

DISTEND is a combination of the prefix *dis-*, in this case meaning *apart*, and *tend*, from a Latin word meaning to *stretch*. The *tend* root is also found in such words as *extend*, *contend*, and *intend*. To DISTEND is to stretch out or swell, especially because of internal pressure.

> "The balloon gradually DISTENDED as we filled it with water."
> "His stomach was DISTENDED with gas."

The most common wrong answer is *postpone*, possibly because the *dis* and *end* parts of the word suggest "not ending," and thus putting something off.

Other forms of the word: DISTENSION or
DISTENTION, n.

Exercise 1

Answer each question with a YES or NO. Put a check in the space for YES or NO next to each question.

		Yes	No
1.	Would comments about sports be GERMANE during a discussion of the solar system?	_____	_____
2.	Can GIBES be annoying?	_____	_____
3.	Would an actor try to give an INIMITABLE performance?	_____	_____
4.	Are librarians usually ITINERANT?	_____	_____
5.	Do television announcers usually have MELLIFLUOUS voices?	_____	_____
6.	Would a PUGNACIOUS person be likely to get into a fight?	_____	_____
7.	Would opera AFICIONADOS have little interest in music?	_____	_____
8.	Do you lose something when you CEDE it?	_____	_____
9.	Would most people find it unpleasant to be DEBASED?	_____	_____
10.	Did Thomas Paine want to FOMENT a rebellion in the British Colonies in America?	_____	_____
11.	Would a stubborn person be likely to show FORBEARANCE?	_____	_____
12.	Would a JOCOSE person be likely to scowl?	_____	_____
13.	Would a detective find an unsolved murder case VEXING?	_____	_____
14.	Can a friendship BURGEON?	_____	_____
15.	Can cheeks DISTEND?	_____	_____

Exercise 2

Each sentence contains a test word in CAPITAL letters. Decide whether the test word is being used correctly or incorrectly in the sentence. Put a check in the space for RIGHT or WRONG next to the sentence.

		Right	Wrong
1.	Your comments are not GERMANE to the topic at hand.	_____	_____
2.	Bill thought it was immature to GIBE at someone just for being different.	_____	_____
3.	When Charlie started showing up for work late, the result was INIMITABLE: he was fired.	_____	_____
4.	The ITINERANT life of the traveling salesman became too much for him as he grew older.	_____	_____
5.	I could listen to her MELLIFLUOUS voice forever.	_____	_____
6.	Harry was PUGNACIOUS to get as much money as he could before it was too late.	_____	_____
7.	He is a true AFICIONADO of wine; there is nothing he doesn't know about the subject.	_____	_____
8.	The judge CEDED the money from them and awarded it to us.	_____	_____
9.	The atomic bomb totally DEBASED the city.	_____	_____

10. The warden said a few ringleaders had FOMENTED the riot in the prison.   ——   ——

11. The coach is showing amazing FORBEARANCE; I would have thrown Paul off the team weeks ago.   ——   ——

12. His JOCOSE comments were out of place at the solemn gathering.   ——   ——

13. The teacher was VEXED by the lack of obedience in the classroom.   ——   ——

14. They BURGEONED in to tell us the exciting news.   ——   ——

15. The more he ate, the more his stomach would DISTEND.   ——   ——

Exercise 3

Each test word is followed by three other words. Decide which of the three words is LEAST CLOSELY RELATED in its meaning to the meaning of the test word. Put the letter for the word you choose in the space at the end of the line.

EXAMPLE

    TINY: **a)** small   **b)** short   **c)** angry   __C__

1. GERMANE: **a)** expected   **b)** apropos   **c)** pertinent   ——

2. GIBE: **a)** scoff   **b)** sneer   **c)** smile   ——

3. INIMITABLE: **a)** illustrious   **b)** banal   **c)** unique   ——

4. ITINERANT: **a)** vagabond   **b)** thief   **c)** nomad   ——

5. MELLIFLUOUS: **a)** smooth   **b)** light   **c)** sweet   ——

6. PUGNACIOUS: **a)** opposing   **b)** aggressive   **c)** hostile   ——

7. AFICIONADO: **a)** agitator   **b)** zealot   **c)** fan   ——

8. CEDE: **a)** lend   **b)** grant   **c)** surrender   ——

9. DEBASE: **a)** corrupt   **b)** lower   **c)** harm   ——

10. FOMENT: **a)** agitate   **b)** incite   **c)** debate   ——

11. FORBEARANCE: **a)** long suffering   **b)** unhappiness   **c)** understanding   ——

12. JOCOSE: **a)** facetious   **b)** amiable   **c)** mellifluous   ——

13. VEX: **a)** pester   **b)** dismiss   **c)** confuse   ——

14. BURGEON: **a)** live   **b)** flower   **c)** grow   ——

15. DISTEND: **a)** extend   **b)** inflate   **c)** disappear   ——

Chapter 6

Pretest

Each test word is printed in CAPITAL letters. From the five choices on the next line, select the one which comes nearest in meaning to the meaning of the test word. Underline the one you select.

1. INTIMATION
   friendship   suggestion   thought   threat   solution
2. INVIOLATE
   intact   injured   kindly   beautiful   new
3. LUMINARY
   optimist   student   priest   substitute   celebrity
4. PANACHE
   delight   jollity   flair   care   despair
5. to PARRY
   give back   annoy   imitate   ward off   seek out
6. SURREPTITIOUS
   apparent   secret   destructive   celebrated   evil
7. to UPBRAID
   praise   teach   hang   scold   correct
8. DISPARATE
   unlike   identical   unprepared   frightening   far off
9. PECUNIARY
   involuntary   psychological   monetary   official   joyous
10. PROVISO
    request   stipulation   assistance   preparation   agreement
11. REMISS
    careless   crazy   irritating   confused   cowardly
12. STIGMA
    fame   rumor   pain   stain   disease
13. to TRUNCATE
    extend   cut short   twirl   gather up   hide
14. VAPID
    lifeless   bubbly   muddy   entertaining   pretty
15. ABSTEMIOUS
    extravagant   stern   sparing   secret   healthy

INTIMATION (in-tə-mA'-shən) n.: a suggestion, hint

To INTIMATE (in'-tə-mAt) something is to communicate it subtly and indirectly, usually in order to be discreet rather than to be misleading.

> "Janice INTIMATED that she might be busy that night and that Bill should find another date for the party."

INTIMATION is the noun form of INTIMATE.

> "There was no INTIMATION of wrongdoing in the report; it merely stated that standard procedures had not been followed."

> "We were all worried by the INTIMATION that John's inquiry was more serious than we had thought."

Other forms of the word: INTIMATE, v.

INVIOLATE (in-vI'-ə-lit) adj.: intact, undisturbed, unprofaned

One meaning of *violate* is to *harm* or *disturb,* as in the sentence, "The presence of the unbeliever *violated* the sacredness of the temple." Something that is INVIOLATE has *not* been violated in this sense. See *in-*₂ under Prefixes. The word is used about people, objects, institutions, and the like that are free from being attacked or profaned.

> "The enemy bombers destroyed most of the city, but hospitals and churches were left INVIOLATE."

> "The president said he would cut the budget, but that Social Security would be INVIOLATE."

> "This promise must be kept INVIOLATE; if you break it, you will be punished."

The most common wrong answer on the Pretest is *injured,* probably chosen because of *violate.*

LUMINARY (lU'-mə-ner-E) n.: a celebrity, notable, leading light

LUMINARY is derived from a Latin word for *light,* also the source of *luminous* and *illuminate.* A LUMINARY is a celestial body, such as the sun, that gives light. But the word is usually used in a figurative sense of a person who is eminent in his or her field, a "leading light."

> "All the greatest LUMINARIES of the literary world were at the dinner."

> "The medical society was astonished by the bitter disagreement between the two LUMINARIES of the profession."

> "She was at best a minor LUMINARY in the galaxy of Hollywood stars."

PANACHE (pə-nash' or pə-nahsh') n.: flair, verve, dash, swagger

The basic meaning of PANACHE is "a plume of feathers worn as an ornament on a helmet or cap." From this it has come to be used for style or flair, such as would be demonstrated by wearing a PANACHE.

> "She did everything with a little bit of PANACHE. She arrived at her college reunion in a hot air balloon."

> "You should dress with more PANACHE. The gray business suits and dark ties you wear are just too dull."

> "The singer is quite talented, but lacks the PANACHE that would make audiences really excited."

PARRY (par'-E) v.: to ward off, deflect, evade

To PARRY something—a blow or a thrust with a sword, for example—is to ward it off.

> "The boxer was unable to PARRY his opponent's barrage of jabs."

> "The fencer easily PARRIED his opponent's feeble thrusts."

PARRY is often used about nonphysical kinds of warding off.

> "The politician skillfully PARRIED the reporter's probing questions."

> "It is useless to try to PARRY his demands; let's just give in to them."

PARRY is also a noun.

> "The president was an expert in the thrust and PARRY of these press conferences."

SURREPTITIOUS (ser-əp-tish'-əs) adj.: secret, clandestine, stealthy, covert

SURREPTITIOUS means "done in a secret or underhanded manner," usually because the action is felt to be improper.

> "Because of their SURREPTITIOUS manner, we knew they were up to no good."
>
> "The shoplifter SURREPTITIOUSLY placed the bracelet into her bag."
>
> "The conservative professor occasionally indulged his SURREPTITIOUS fondness for disco dancing."

UPBRAID (uhp-brAd') v.: to scold, censure, reprove

UPBRAID comes from an Old English word meaning "to throw up against," and means "to scold severely, to reprove vehemently." The word suggests a formal criticism, usually by a superior or an official.

> "The teacher UPBRAIDED the students for smoking in the corridor."
>
> "The policeman UPBRAIDED the motorist for disregarding the safety of others."
>
> "The boys were UPBRAIDED by the lady when they tossed the empty cans on her lawn."

DISPARATE (dis'-pər-it or dis-par'-it) adj.: unlike, dissimilar, distinct, different, diverse

DISPARATE comes from the Latin verb *parare,* meaning to *prepare,* and the prefix *dis-,* which in this case means *apart.* DISPARATE now emphasizes the *apart* rather than the *prepare* of its derivation, and means "completely different, markedly dissimilar."

> "The students come from many DISPARATE backgrounds: some rich, some poor, some raised strictly, others given a great deal of freedom."
>
> "The artist created strange sculptures from such DISPARATE elements as old tires and parts of machines."

The noun DISPARITY means *difference,* and is applied particularly to inequality of age or wealth.

> "If they are truly in love, the DISPARITY between their ages will not matter."

Other forms of the word: DISPARITY, n.

PECUNIARY (pi-kyU'-nE-er-E) adj.: monetary, financial

PECUNIARY comes from the Latin word for *money,* also the source of the word *impecunious,* which means "lacking money." PECUNIARY means "relating to or consisting of money." It is usually used with reference to small-scale or practical matters dealing with money.

> "Alice didn't help us out of friendship but from a PECUNIARY motive—she knew we would pay her."
>
> "There is psychological satisfaction to be gained from this job, but the PECUNIARY rewards are slight."
>
> "Mr. Micawber was always optimistic despite his PECUNIARY difficulties."

PROVISO (prə-vI'-zO) n.: a stipulation, condition, reservation, provision

A PROVISO is a clause in a contract or other agreement that introduces some sort of qualification or limitation. The word PROVISO comes from the Latin phrase *proviso quod,* "provided that," with which such clauses began in documents of the Middle Ages. PROVISO can also be used in a general sense to refer to any stipulation or condition.

> "The contract contained a PROVISO stating that if payments were not made by the end of each month either party could withdraw from the agreement."
>
> "Mrs. Collins let her son go to the party with the PROVISO that he be back by eleven."

Agreement is a common choice on the Pretest. People who choose it are aware that a PROVISO has something to do with an agreement, but aren't quite sure what.

REMISS (ri-mis') adj.: careless, inattentive, negligent

REMISS means "careless or negligent in attending to one's duty." It is often used after the noun it modifies.

> "Sharon is REMISS about doing her homework."
>
> "The lawyer was REMISS in not informing his client of her rights."

Occasionally the word is applied to the duty itself and means "showing negligence."

> "Her reports have been REMISS; she should have shown how she reached her conclusions, instead of just stating them as facts."

STIGMA (stig'-mə) n.: a stain, brand, mark of disgrace

STIGMA comes from the Greek word for *tattoo*. Originally in English a STIGMA was a mark made by a branding iron on the skin of a slave or criminal. From this it came to be used figuratively about any mark of shame or disgrace.

> "The ex-convict tried to overcome the STIGMA of his criminal record."
> "She felt there was a STIGMA attached to being on welfare, so she refused to apply for it."
> "He thought his rural accent was a STIGMA that marked him as a yokel."

The verb from STIGMA is STIGMATIZE, which means "to mark with a STIGMA, to brand as disgraceful."

> "The speaker said he didn't mean to STIGMATIZE all college students as lazy and stupid."

Other forms of the word: STIGMATIZE, v.

TRUNCATE (truhng'-kAt) v.: to cut short, lop

TRUNCATE is related to the word *trunk*. The *trunk* is the main part of anything. The *trunk* of a human body, for example, is the central part of it, excluding the head and the limbs. To TRUNCATE something is to cut it short by lopping off part of it.

> "The mountain's peak appears to have been TRUNCATED by an ancient volcanic eruption."
> "They had to TRUNCATE their presentation when they ran out of time."
> "The cross-country trip had to be TRUNCATED in Denver because of a lack of funds."
> "Craig's session at the computer terminal was TRUNCATED when the system went down."

VAPID (vap'-id) adj.: lifeless, flat, uninteresting, insipid

VAPID means "lacking taste, life, or spirit." The word is sometimes used about wine, beer, or other drinks that have become flat and tasteless. It is more often used about people and their intellectual activities.

> "This movie is utterly VAPID. It doesn't have the slightest bit of intellectual or human interest."
> "The VAPID young man spent all of his time watching game shows on television."
> "She had the same VAPID smile for everything and everyone; clearly she didn't understand a bit of what was going on."

Bubbly is the most popular wrong answer. In one sense this is almost an opposite of VAPID. A person with a bubbly manner may also be VAPID, and this may cause the confusion.

Other forms of the word: VAPIDITY, n.

ABSTEMIOUS (ab-stE'-mE-əs) adj.: sparing, abstinent

To be ABSTEMIOUS is to be moderate and self-restrained, especially in eating and drinking.

> "The ABSTEMIOUS gentleman never had more than an occasional glass of wine."
> "Far from being ABSTEMIOUS, he indulged to the fullest in every pleasure."

In a slightly different sense ABSTEMIOUS can mean "characterized by moderation," *sparing*.

> "Her ABSTEMIOUS diet consisted of little more than bread and water."

Exercise 1

Answer each question with a YES or NO. Put a check in the space for YES or NO next to each question.

		Yes	No
1.	Would an INTIMATION be blunt?	———	———
2.	Can a custom be INVIOLATE?	———	———
3.	Was Albert Einstein a scientific LUMINARY?	———	———
4.	Do some great entertainers have PANACHE?	———	———
5.	Will a PARRY generally wound an opponent?	———	———
6.	Would a spying mission usually be carried out SURREPTITIOUSLY?	———	———
7.	Are mischievous children likely to be UPBRAIDED?	———	———
8.	Are love and hate DISPARATE emotions?	———	———
9.	Would a bankrupt business be suffering from PECUNIARY difficulties?	———	———
10.	Do some contracts contain PROVISOS?	———	———
11.	Would a shiftless teacher be REMISS in his duties?	———	———
12.	Could a person's continual lying become a STIGMA?	———	———
13.	Can a trip be TRUNCATED?	———	———
14.	Can a book be VAPID?	———	———
15.	Is a drunkard ABSTEMIOUS?	———	———

Exercise 2

Each sentence contains a test word in CAPITAL letters. Decide whether the test word is being used correctly or incorrectly in the sentence. Put a check in the space for RIGHT or WRONG next to the sentence.

		Right	Wrong
1.	The boss INTIMATED that there might be a promotion for Ted if he did a good job.	———	———
2.	The play's director left nothing—not even Hamlet's soliloquies—INVIOLATE.	———	———
3.	Simpson wasn't a LUMINARY in the business world, but he was respected by those who knew him.	———	———
4.	The students rented a Rolls-Royce so that they would arrive at the prom with PANACHE.	———	———
5.	The boss PARRIED Bill's request for a raise by telling him to work harder.	———	———
6.	The police became SURREPTITIOUS of the men driving the truck down the alley.	———	———
7.	The boss UPBRAIDED her workers for constantly arriving late.	———	———
8.	We were DISPARATE to go to the beach that hot day.	———	———
9.	PECUNIARY problems are making it difficult for me to pay my bills.	———	———

10. The college admitted Bill with the PROVISO that he take a remedial writing course.

11. Bill's mother told him he was REMISS in not giving her the telephone message.

12. Once the principal had STIGMATIZED them as troublemakers, they had a hard time living down their reputation.

13. The director TRUNCATED the play by leaving out the last two scenes.

14. The VAPID girl did nothing but read movie magazines and go to parties.

15. John has an ABSTEMIOUS lifestyle: he spends very little on entertainment.

Exercise 3

Each test word is followed by three other words. Decide which of the three words is LEAST CLOSELY RELATED in its meaning to the meaning of the test word. Put the letter for the word you choose in the space at the end of the line.

EXAMPLE

	TINY:	**a)** small	**b)** short	**c)** angry	C
1.	INTIMATION:	**a)** whisper	**b)** lie	**c)** suggestion	
2.	INVIOLATE:	**a)** refined	**b)** venerated	**c)** protected	
3.	LUMINARY:	**a)** eminent	**b)** notable	**c)** notorious	
4.	PANACHE:	**a)** expense	**b)** flamboyance	**c)** style	
5.	PARRY:	**a)** dodge	**b)** deflect	**c)** stab	
6.	SURREPTITIOUS:	**a)** stubborn	**b)** secretive	**c)** clandestine	
7.	UPBRAID:	**a)** admonish	**b)** berate	**c)** convince	
8.	DISPARATE:	**a)** unnecessary	**b)** divergent	**c)** unequal	
9.	PECUNIARY:	**a)** federal	**b)** fiscal	**c)** financial	
10.	PROVISO:	**a)** bargain	**b)** condition	**c)** requirement	
11.	REMISS:	**a)** lax	**b)** wan	**c)** slipshod	
12.	STIGMA:	**a)** shame	**b)** disgrace	**c)** ruin	
13.	TRUNCATE:	**a)** hide	**b)** abbreviate	**c)** lop	
14.	VAPID:	**a)** insipid	**b)** vivacious	**c)** banal	
15.	ABSTEMIOUS:	**a)** starving	**b)** abstinent	**c)** sober	

Review Test—Chapters 4–6

Fill in each blank with the test word (or a form of the test word) which best fits the sentence. Use the words listed below.

AMITY	INIMITABLE	OBDURATE	PROVISO	TRAVAIL
AUSPICIOUS	INVIOLATE	PARITY	SHIFTLESS	TRUNCATE
DISCERN	JOCOSE	PARRY	SURREPTITIOUS	UPBRAID
GIBE	MELLIFLUOUS	PAUCITY	TRANSGRESS	VEX
GUILE				

1. These _____ fellows just can't be serious; everything is a joke to them.

2. With only two minutes left in the class, the professor was forced to _____ his lecture.

3. Mrs. Sims was so _____ by her children's constant questioning that she finally shouted at them to be quiet.

4. Despite a few problems, the two nations shared the same border in relative _____ .

5. The custom of having Thanksgiving dinner at our house is _____; nothing has ever made us change it.

6. Samuel Johnson's literary style was _____; no one could hope to match its vigor and precision.

7. The color-blind boy was unable to _____ the difference between red and green.

8. The company's lawyer inserted a(n) _____ in the contract.

9. The judge _____ the lawyers for wasting his time with their trivial objections.

10. Mr. Phillips remained _____ and said he would never rehire the worker he had fired.

11. The sweetness of the singer's _____ voice charmed us all.

12. Few of the laborers could endure for very long the _____ of dragging the boulders across the hot desert.

13. There is such a(n) _____ of good books in the local library that no one bothers to go there.

14. Sam _____ at his friends for having voted for a politician who turned out to be a crook.

15. Just because I'm unemployed, that doesn't mean I'm (a)n _____ good-for-nothing. I'd work hard, if only I could find a job.

16. It only took us two seasons to achieve _____ with the other teams in the league; now we're as good as any of them.

17. The king decreed that all who _____ this law should be put to death.

18. The actor forgot his lines in the first scene of the play; it was hardly a(n) _____ beginning.

19. Through cunning and _____, he was able to convince everyone that his opponent was unfit for office.

20. The boxer managed to _____ his opponent's blows, but he was unable to land a punch himself.

21. No one noticed the prisoner's _____ movements toward the open door.

39

Fill in each blank with the test word (or a form of the test word) which best fits the sentence. Use the words listed below.

ABSTEMIOUS	COMMISERATE	FORBEARANCE	LUMINARY	REMISS
AFICIONADO	DEBASE	GERMANE	PANACHE	STIGMA
ASCRIBE	DISPARATE	GLOWER	PECUNIARY	VAPID
BURGEON	DISTEND	INTIMATION	PONDEROUS	WAN
CEDE	FOMENT	ITINERANT	PUGNACIOUS	

22. The newspaper claimed that the police were _____ in not investigating the charges more thoroughly.

23. The professor's _____ lecture was so dull it put most of his students to sleep.

24. The radicals planned to _____ a rebellion by making fiery speeches and calling for a general strike.

25. His comments, though interesting, were not _____ to the subject under discussion.

26. Almost overnight the shy young girl seemed to _____ into a self-confident woman.

27. Dave's friends _____ with him when he failed to get the job.

28. The _____ farmhands traveled all across the state, picking up jobs here and there.

29. The animal's body was so _____ that it looked round.

30. The _____ truckdriver was ready to fight anyone who got in his way on the road.

31. Pamela's long hours of studying have left her looking quite _____. She needs rest and relaxation.

32. The army took these _____ types of men and molded them into an effective fighting force.

33. The judges decided to _____ his behavior to ignorance of the rules, not cheating.

34. Cindy refused to _____ herself by appearing in the ridiculous costume. She said she had too much dignity.

35. We were surprised by John's _____ that he might not be working for us much longer.

36. The salesman refused to discuss the _____ aspects of the deal; he said the money would take care of itself.

37. The judge _____ at the noisy spectators and threatened to throw them out of the courtroom.

38. I'm sorry I'm so late in repaying you; your _____ is greatly appreciated.

39. His comments on current affairs were utterly _____; he had nothing new or interesting to say.

40. The country refused to _____ any of the territory it had captured in the war.

41. The comic-book _____ has a complete collection of *Superman*.

42. Many Hall-of-Famers and other athletic _____ were on the physical-fitness panel.

43. He tried hard to remove the _____ attached to the family name because of his father's crimes.

44. The _____ man ate and drank only when absolutely necessary.

45. The actor had a certain _____ that made even his smallest roles interesting and exciting.

Chapter 7

Pretest

Each test word is printed in CAPITAL letters. From the five choices on the next line, select the one which comes nearest in meaning to the meaning of the test word. Underline the one you select.

1. FLACCID
   bitter   peaceful   flabby   false   messy

2. to DAUNT
   hearten   discourage   challenge   insult   trick

3. to MESMERIZE
   scandalize   hypnotize   bewilder   enchant   deceive

4. PEEVISH
   hateful   fearful   nearsighted   stingy   irritable

5. PRODIGY
   waste   hope   knowledge   marvel   threat

6. TENET
   example   feeling   belief   conclusion   rumor

7. DOLOROUS
   mournful   soothing   dull   cheerful   glowing

8. FRETFUL
   awful   frightened   peaceful   irritable   proud

9. PROGENY
   relatives   followers   talents   ancestors   descendants

10. AMBIENCE
    perfume   environment   weariness   horizon   state of mind

11. CATACLYSM
    battle   jamboree   cliff   disaster   disappointment

12. DEMISE
    death   illness   birth   misfortune   departure

13. HINTERLAND
    city   kingdom   backcountry   hilly area   tropics

14. IMBROGLIO
    celebration   romance   defeat   comedy   predicament

15. MISCREANT
    ghost   beginner   loser   evildoer   moron

FLACCID (flak'-səd or flas'-əd) adj.: flabby, limp

FLACCID means "soft and limp; not firm." It is usually used about physical things such as flesh.

> "Bill's muscles became FLACCID from lack of exercise."

FLACCID is also used in an extended sense about anything that lacks firmness or vigor.

> "Under Smith's FLACCID leadership the company lacked drive and direction."

Other forms of the word: FLACCIDITY, n.

DAUNT (dônt) v.: to discourage, dismay, intimidate

DAUNT is related to the word *dominate*. Both come from a Latin word meaning to *master* or *tame*. To DAUNT is to dishearten or intimidate by removing the courage a person needs to achieve something.

> "He was completely DAUNTED by the years of study it would take to become a doctor."
>
> "Nothing DAUNTED the climbers in their attempt to scale Mount Everest."

The related words DAUNTLESS and UNDAUNTED are perhaps more common. Both mean "not discouraged," *resolute, bold*.

> "The DAUNTLESS explorers went where no man had ever been before."

The most commonly chosen wrong answer for DAUNT on the Pretest is *challenge*. DAUNTING involves a challenge, but the emphasis is on the discouragement and dismay that the challenge causes.

Other forms of the word: DAUNTLESS, adj.
UNDAUNTED, adj.

MESMERIZE (mez'-mə-rIz or mes'-mə-rIz) v.: to hypnotize, spellbind, enthrall

MESMERIZE comes from the name Franz Anton Mesmer, an eighteenth-century Austrian physician who was one of the early practicers of hypnotism. The first meaning of MESMERIZE is literally to *hypnotize*, but it is more often used in the extended sense of *fascinate*, to "have a hypnotic effect upon." A person who is MESMERIZED behaves as if hypnotized.

> "When the actors finished the scene, there was a moment of silence; the audience had been so MESMERIZED that it forgot to clap."
>
> "When she started to sing, I was MESMERIZED: I couldn't move or speak."

Other forms of the word: MESMERISM, n.

PEEVISH (pE'-vish) adj.: irritable, cross, fretful, querulous

A person who is PEEVISH is irritable in a childish, petty way, and reacts to minor problems like a spoiled child.

> "Joe noticed that his father was becoming more PEEVISH: if his dinner was late, he would call the nurse names."
>
> "When her mother asked her to do the dishes, Betty sighed and PEEVISHLY stomped into the kitchen."
>
> "The PEEVISH doctor grew angry whenever anything was out of its proper place."

Other forms of the word: PEEVE, v., n.

PRODIGY (prod'-ə-jE) n.: a marvel, wonder; a person with exceptional talent

PRODIGY comes from a Latin word meaning an *omen* or a *portent*. In English PRODIGY originally had the same meaning and referred to an extraordinary event or occurrence that might be a prophetic sign. It then came to be used about anything that might cause one to marvel or wonder.

> "The lecturer spoke about comets, supernovae, and other astronomical PRODIGIES."

The word is most commonly used today about a person, especially a child, who has extraordinary talent or ability.

> "Mozart was a musical PRODIGY. He composed his first pieces when he was only four."
>
> "Billy's parents thought he was a child PRODIGY, but no one else thought he was very talented."

TENET (ten'-ət) n.: a belief, dogma, doctrine

TENET comes from a Latin word meaning to *hold,* also the source of the word *tenacious.* A TENET is a firmly held belief. The word is used especially about principles or doctrines believed by a group of people or an organization.

> "One of the religion's fundamental TENETS is that the world will end in the year 2075."

> "He approved of the organization's TENETS but not of its actions."

> " 'Equal pay for equal work' was one of the TENETS of the women's group."

DOLOROUS (dO'-lə-rəs or dol-ə-rəs) adj.: mournful, sorrowful, melancholy, lugubrious

DOLOR is a Latin word meaning *sorrow, grief.* It is also used in English as a poetic or literary synonym for *sorrow.* The adjective DOLOROUS, meaning *sorrowful, melancholy,* is more common. See *-ous* under Suffixes. It too has a somewhat literary flavor, and is occasionally used rather humorously for grief that is exaggerated or excessive.

> "After a few days Hal began to find the DOLOROUS sound of the fog horn to be quite depressing."

> "Her DOLOROUS sobs put everyone in a sad mood."

> "I had to interrupt her DOLOROUS tale of woe to tell her I was late for an appointment."

Other forms of the word: DOLOR, n.

FRETFUL (fret'-fəl) adj.: irritable, peevish, petulant, querulous

FRETFUL is difficult apparently because it looks like *fearful,* leading many people to select *frightened* as its synonym. The verb to FRET comes from an Old English word meaning to *devour.* In modern English it can mean to *eat into* or *corrode,* but usually it is used in a figurative sense to mean to *worry, be troubled.* The word usually suggests complaining and irritation, rather than serious worry.

> "She FRETTED for days until she heard that the package had arrived."

FRETFUL is the adjective from this meaning of FRET. See *-ful* under Suffixes.

> "The FRETFUL children complained constantly during the long bus ride."

> "Everyone in the office became FRETFUL and short-tempered when the air-conditioning broke down."

Other forms of the word: FRET, v.

PROGENY (proj'-ə-nE) n.: descendants, offspring

PROGENY may be either singular or plural, but it is usually used as plural. PROGENY are descendants of a mother or father. They may be either immediate offspring or more remote descendants. The word is usually used about humans, but may be applied to plants or animals as well.

> "Many of Johann Sebastian Bach's PROGENY also became distinguished musicians."

> "Only a few of her PROGENY inherited her rare disease."

PROGENY can also be used in an extended sense, about people or things that are like descendants.

> "Freud's intellectual PROGENY have dominated psychiatry."

AMBIENCE (am'-bE-əns) n.: environment, milieu

AMBIENCE is often spelled AMBIANCE. AMBIENCE comes from the French and occasionally keeps its French pronunciation: om-byons'.

The latin prefix *ambi-* means *on both sides, around.* It is found in the word *ambidextrous,* which means "able to use both hands equally well." AMBIENCE means "the surrounding atmosphere," the *environment* or *milieu.*

> "Gerald flourished in the challenging intellectual AMBIENCE of the Ivy League school."

> "The decor and the soft lighting create a pleasant, intimate AMBIENCE in the restaurant."

> "The meeting took place in an AMBIENCE of hostility and mutual resentment."

43

CATACLYSM (kat'-ə-kliz-əm) n.: a disaster, catastrophe, violent upheaval

A CATACLYSM is a sudden, violent upheaval. It can be physical, like an earthquake or a flood.

"Scientists predicted that a CATACLYSM would devastate the western part of the country."

Or it can be a social or political upheaval, like a revolution.

"The CATACLYSM of the French Revolution brought about a change in the social order."

"He argued that gradual change was preferable to a CATACLYSM that might destroy the good things along with the bad."

Other forms of the word: CATACLYSMIC, adj.

DEMISE (də-mIz') n.: death

DEMISE is a somewhat literary synonym for *death*.

"We were all shocked by her sudden DEMISE; she had never been sick a day in her life."

DEMISE is also used in a figurative sense for the end of anything's existence.

"The availability of cheap imports brought about the DEMISE of the shoe industry in New England."

"The opposition of several key legislators ensured the bill's DEMISE in Congress."

The most common wrong answer on the Pretest is *misfortune,* which is close in meaning but certainly not synonymous.

HINTERLAND (hin'-tər-land) n.: backcountry, remote area, interior region

HINTERLAND comes from the word *land* and the German word *hinter,* which means *behind, rear.* The HINTERLAND is the land behind a coast that may provide trade goods for a port. In an extended use, HINTERLAND is applied to any sort of remote region, far from a metropolitan area.

"When Ellen was tired of the crowded city, she loved to be out in the HINTERLANDS where she wouldn't see a soul for days."

"It took several months for news of the war to reach the HINTERLANDS."

"Carl's favorite subject for photography was the lonely, rugged HINTERLAND."

IMBROGLIO (im-brOl'-yO) n.: a predicament, confused situation, entanglement

Note the pronunciation. IMBROGLIO is from the Italian, and keeps its Italian pronunciation. An IMBROGLIO is a confused or perplexing state of affairs, particularly one that results in a misunderstanding or a disagreement.

"The IMBROGLIO over the diplomat's arrest almost led to a war between the two countries."

"The billionaire's death caused quite an IMBROGLIO about who would inherit his money."

"The dispute over who would pay the caterer caused an IMBROGLIO between the two families at the wedding reception."

MISCREANT (mis'-krE-ənt) n.: a villain, scoundrel, evildoer; an infidel, heretic

MISCREANT originally comes from Latin words meaning "not believing," and was originally used about a person whose religious beliefs were thought to be false, a *nonbeliever* or *heretic.* It is still used in this way, but it is used more often with a meaning developed from this original sense: *villain* or *evildoer.*

"The police chief promised that the MISCREANTS who had vandalized the church would be arrested soon."

"The man said that Jimmy was a young MISCREANT who should be punished severely."

"The vicious MISCREANTS lurked in the alley waiting for someone to rob."

Exercise 1

Answer each question with a YES or NO. Put a check in the space for YES or NO next to each question.

		Yes	No
1.	Would a marathon runner have a FLACCID body?	_____	_____
2.	Can the cost of something be DAUNTING?	_____	_____
3.	Can a voice MESMERIZE?	_____	_____
4.	Would it be difficult to irritate a PEEVISH person?	_____	_____
5.	Could a four-hundred-pound pumpkin be called a PRODIGY?	_____	_____
6.	Is a belief in God a TENET of most religions?	_____	_____
7.	Can music be DOLOROUS?	_____	_____
8.	Would a nonchalant person usually be FRETFUL?	_____	_____
9.	Are babies PROGENY?	_____	_____
10.	Can the lighting affect the AMBIENCE in a restaurant?	_____	_____
11.	Was the Russian Revolution a CATACLYSM?	_____	_____
12.	Would most people feel sad over the DEMISE of a parent?	_____	_____
13.	Are the HINTERLANDS crowded?	_____	_____
14.	Is an IMBROGLIO likely to lead to an argument?	_____	_____
15.	Is a criminal a MISCREANT?	_____	_____

Exercise 2

Each sentence contains a test word in CAPITAL letters. Decide whether the test word is being used correctly or incorrectly in the sentence. Put a check in the space for RIGHT or WRONG next to the sentence.

		Right	Wrong
1.	They spent a FLACCID day on the beach just swimming and relaxing.	_____	_____
2.	John was DAUNTED by the prospect of having to look for a new job.	_____	_____
3.	The teacher MESMERIZED the material so quickly we couldn't understand it.	_____	_____
4.	The boy complained PEEVISHLY that he never got a chance to play quarterback.	_____	_____
5.	He lost his PRODIGY when he was quite young, and never entirely regained it.	_____	_____
6.	The TENET that all men are created equal is basic in American political thought.	_____	_____
7.	In a DOLOROUS tone of voice Kathy told us all about her cat's illness.	_____	_____
8.	The children were so FRETFUL of the movie monster that they had nightmares.	_____	_____
9.	When the rich man died, his numerous PROGENY all claimed part of his estate.	_____	_____

10. John found it impossible to work in the unpleasant AMBIENCE of a noisy and messy office.

11. These prehistoric CATACLYSMS changed the face of the earth.

12. The company's DEMISE was attributed to poor planning by management.

13. People in the cities love the politician, but in the HINTERLANDS he is regarded with suspicion.

14. The IMBROGLIO between the governor and the legislature over the budget finally landed in the courts.

15. The principal promptly expelled the MISCREANTS who had attacked the teacher.

Exercise 3

Each test word is followed by three other words. Decide which of the three words is LEAST CLOSELY RELATED in its meaning to the meaning of the test word. Put the letter for the word you choose in the space at the end of the line.

EXAMPLE

	TINY:	a) small	b) short	c) angry	C
1.	FLACCID:	a) flimsy	b) listless	c) hollow	
2.	DAUNT:	a) destroy	b) vex	c) confound	
3.	MESMERIZE:	a) enthrall	b) tranquilize	c) hypnotize	
4.	PEEVISH:	a) quarrelsome	b) fierce	c) petty	
5.	PRODIGY:	a) talent	b) fighter	c) wonder	
6.	TENET:	a) rumor	b) opinion	c) principle	
7.	DOLOROUS:	a) sorrowful	b) stubborn	c) doleful	
8.	FRETFUL:	a) restless	b) peevish	c) jocose	
9.	PROGENY:	a) sons	b) cousins	c) grandchildren	
10.	AMBIENCE:	a) milieu	b) background	c) area	
11.	CATACLYSM:	a) calamity	b) upheaval	c) controversy	
12.	DEMISE:	a) suffering	b) extinction	c) death	
13.	HINTERLAND:	a) city	b) interior	c) backcountry	
14.	IMBROGLIO:	a) ambush	b) fracas	c) altercation	
15.	MISCREANT:	a) nonbeliever	b) villain	c) inventor	

Chapter 8

Pretest

Each test word is printed in CAPITAL letters. From the five choices on the next line, select the one which comes nearest in meaning to the meaning of the test word. Underline the one you select.

1. to QUAFF
    eat   laugh   drink   scratch   cough
2. CHOLERIC
    bad tempered   dying   passive   energetic   underfed
3. DULCET
    boring   sweet   harsh   bland   smooth
4. OBSEQUIOUS
    stern   helpful   crafty   fawning   reverent
5. to REMUNERATE
    pay   promote   fine   award   recount
6. TIMOROUS
    nasty   quiet   loving   tiny   fearful
7. CHURLISH
    helpful   rude   silly   greedy   ugly
8. to DILATE
    waver   decline   expand   harden   contract
9. HIATUS
    problem   shelter   gap   rumor   extension
10. LASSITUDE
    poverty   desire   happiness   greed   weariness
11. PETULANT
    quick   friendly   popular   irritable   cunning
12. REVERIE
    daydream   prayer   conversation   task   judgment
13. SAGACIOUS
    absurd   shrewd   obscure   courteous   renowned
14. DIRE
    hideous   uncertain   complex   complete   fearful
15. EBULLIENCE
    brilliance   enthusiasm   unhappiness   fatness   humor

QUAFF (kwof or kwaf) v.: to drink deeply

To QUAFF is to drink deeply and heartily, to drain a cup or glass.

> "Falstaff QUAFFED the tankard of ale in one long swallow, then called for more."

> "The tired athlete QUAFFED the refreshing drink."

> "I knew you were thirsty, but I didn't expect you to QUAFF the whole pitcher of lemonade."

CHOLERIC (kol'-ə-rik or kə-ler'-ik) adj.: bad-tempered, irascible

In the Middle Ages, anger was thought to be caused by an excess of CHOLER, or yellow bile, in the body. The adjective CHOLERIC (see -ic under Suffixes) is used about people who are easily made angry, who have irritable or touchy dispositions.

> "As he got older, Mr. Finn became CHOLERIC; he would fly into rages over small matters."

> "Jane's CHOLERIC nature made her difficult to deal with."

> "The CHOLERIC patient became furious with the nurses when they wouldn't cater to his every whim."

Other forms of the word: CHOLER, n.

DULCET (duhl'-sit) adj.: sweet, melodious

DULCET comes from an Old French word meaning "sweet," and originally meant "sweet to the taste" in English. Over time, however, its meaning changed to "sweet to the ear," *melodious*.

> "When the soldier was feverish, only the nurse's DULCET voice could soothe him."

> "The flute, when played well, has a particularly DULCET sound."

OBSEQUIOUS (ob-sE'-kwE-əs) adj.: fawning, servile

OBSEQUIOUS means "excessively polite." The word usually has a negative connotation and suggests flattery and groveling, although it may only suggest extreme obedience and attentiveness.

> "The boss didn't like OBSEQUIOUS employees who would constantly open doors for him and compliment his ideas."

> "The service at the restaurant was friendly but not OBSEQUIOUS."

> "The OBSEQUIOUS servants said that nothing would give them more pleasure than to do our bidding."

Crafty is more popular than the correct answer—*fawning*—on the Pretest, perhaps because OBSEQUIOUS people often seem to be up to something with their insincere flattery; or *crafty* may be chosen because of confusion with the word *devious*.

REMUNERATE (ri-myU'-nə-rAt) v.: to pay for, pay to

REMUNERATE is a somewhat formal synonym for *pay*. It is especially used about payments for services rendered or losses incurred.

> "We offered to REMUNERATE them for the time they had spent helping us."

> "If you become my assistant I will REMUNERATE you handsomely."

In a slightly different sense, REMUNERATE can mean to *pay for* or to *reward*.

> "The boss REMUNERATED our efforts with a large bonus."

REMUNERATION is the act of REMUNERATING, or a payment, a recompense.

> "Art was troubled by his inadequate REMUNERATION and demanded more money."

Other forms of the word: REMUNERATION, n.

TIMOROUS (tim'-ər-əs) adj.: fearful, timid, apprehensive

TIMOROUS comes from the Latin word for *fear*, also the source of the word *timid*. A person who is TIMOROUS is easily intimidated and is afraid to do things, such as make decisions or be self-assertive.

> "Paul grew so TIMOROUS once inside the deserted house that he couldn't go forward or leave; he was frozen to the spot with fear."

> "The TIMOROUS clerk couldn't get up the courage to ask his boss for a raise."

> "Susie is so TIMOROUS she is apprehensive about leaving the house."

The most commonly chosen wrong answer is *quiet*. TIMOROUS people are usually quiet, but TIMOROUS means *fearful*.

CHURLISH (chɘr'-lish) adj.: rude, boorish, loutish

A CHURL was originally a man of the lowest class in England. The word then came to refer to a person having the qualities thought to be characteristic of a CHURL: rudeness, surliness, vulgarity. CHURLISH is the adjective from CHURL; see -ish under Suffixes.

"The CHURLISH man refused to let the boys cut through his yard."

"The CHURLISH waitress demanded to know if we hade made up our minds yet."

"The bus driver CHURLISHLY told the children to shut up or get out and walk."

Other forms of the word: CHURL, n.

DILATE (dI-lAt') v.: to widen, expand

The *late* part of DILATE comes from a Latin word meaning *wide,* also found in the English word *latitude.* See *di-* under Prefixes. To DILATE is to become wider, to expand. The word is generally used about physical objects.

"The ophthalmologist put some drops in her eyes to make the pupils DILATE."

The word is sometimes used about opinions or subject matter, with the meaning "to speak at length." In this sense DILATE is usually followed by *on* or *upon.*

"The senator DILATED upon his views on fiscal policy."

Other forms of the word: DILATION, n.
DILATATION, n.

HIATUS (hI-A'-tɘs) n.: a gap, interruption, break

A HIATUS is a gap or interval, generally of time or continuity.

"The celebrated actress returned to the stage after a HIATUS of twelve years."

"During the brief HIATUS between appointments, the doctor was able to rest for a few minutes."

"Students used the HIATUS between the end of classes and the beginning of exams to catch up on their reading."

LASSITUDE (las'-ɘ-tUd) n.: weariness, lethargy, languor, listlessness

LASSITUDE is a state of weariness and inactivity, a lack of energy resulting from strain, overwork, a hot climate, or the like.

"Angela couldn't seem to overcome her LASSITUDE; all she wanted to do was lie in bed."

"After the long baseball season the player gave way to a strong feeling of LASSITUDE."

"The muggy, tropical climate induced an overpowering LASSITUDE that made it difficult to work."

PETULANT (pech'-U-lɘnt) adj.: irritable, peevish, ill-tempered

PETULANT means *peevish,* "easily upset or angered," like a spoiled child who doesn't get his or her own way.

"The PETULANT actress became angry every time the director made a suggestion."

"Bob complained PETULANTLY that everyone else always got dessert before he did."

"Rich knew from her PETULANT refusal to greet him that she was angry with him again."

Other forms of the word: PETULANCE, n.

REVERIE (rev'-ɘr-E) n.: a daydream, fanciful musing

REVERIE is sometimes spelled REVERY.

A REVERIE is a daydream, a series of idle thoughts or images.

"Sharon was lost in a REVERIE, thinking about things that happened long ago."

"Jim's REVERIE lasted for an hour before he realized that he had to go to work."

It is also the act of daydreaming.

"The old man spent his days sitting by the lake in quiet REVERIE."

Prayer is a popular choice as the meaning of REVERIE, perhaps because both involve a kind of quiet thought, perhaps because of confusion with the word *revere,* which means to *worship.*

SAGACIOUS (sə-gā′-shəs) adj.: shrewd, astute, judicious, wise

A SAGACIOUS person possesses good judgment, keen penetration, and farsightedness, usually obtained through wide experience.

"The SAGACIOUS lawyer said that these matters took time, but that we should win in the end."

"Through her SAGACIOUS investments in computer stocks she managed to become quite wealthy."

The noun related to SAGACIOUS is SAGACITY.

"Thanks to the SAGACITY of its president, this company has grown steadily over the years."

Other forms of the word: SAGACITY, n.

DIRE (dīr) adj.: fearful, calamitous, disastrous; extreme, urgent

Something that is DIRE causes great fear, either because it is disastrous now, or threatens disaster in the future.

"The general warned of DIRE consequences if the country didn't spend more money on defense."

"The loss of the star center was a DIRE blow to the basketball team."

Often the word places less emphasis on fear and more on urgency or desperation.

"Only in a DIRE emergency would a pupil be allowed to leave school early."

"He was forced to steal out of DIRE necessity; otherwise he would have starved."

EBULLIENCE (i-bul′-yəns) n.: enthusiasm, exuberance, high spirits

See *ex-* under Prefixes. The *bull* part of EBULLIENCE comes from a Latin word meaning to *boil*. EBULLIENCE is a "boiling out" of enthusiasm or exuberance. It suggests an overflowing of feelings or high spirits.

"With his usual EBULLIENCE, the professor talked for an hour about how great and wise Socrates had been."

The adjective from EBULLIENCE is EBULLIENT.

"After the victory, the EBULLIENT coach said that this was the finest team he had ever been associated with."

The most commonly chosen wrong answer is *brilliance,* perhaps because of the similarity in sound, and because both are positive qualities for a person to have.

Other forms of the word: EBULLIENT, adj.

Exercise 1

Answer each question with a YES or NO. Put a check in the space for YES or NO next to each question.

	Yes	No
1. Can you QUAFF food?	_____	_____
2. Would it be fun to live with a CHOLERIC person?	_____	_____
3. Can DULCET sounds be soothing?	_____	_____
4. Would an argumentative person be OBSEQUIOUS?	_____	_____
5. Would workers be angry if they received no REMUNERATION?	_____	_____
6. Are boxing champions usually TIMOROUS?	_____	_____
7. Do CHURLS tend to be pleasant?	_____	_____
8. Can your stomach DILATE?	_____	_____
9. Can a HIATUS last for a long time?	_____	_____
10. Could a boring job cause LASSITUDE?	_____	_____
11. Is it easy to get along with a PETULANT person?	_____	_____
12. Is a REVERIE loud?	_____	_____
13. Would a SAGACIOUS person be likely to go bankrupt?	_____	_____
14. Is an earthquake in a populated area a DIRE event?	_____	_____
15. Would learning about a tragedy cause EBULLIENCE?	_____	_____

Exercise 2

Each sentence contains a test word in CAPITAL letters. Decide whether the test word is being used correctly or incorrectly in the sentence. Put a check in the space for RIGHT or WRONG next to the sentence.

	Right	Wrong
1. We didn't mean to be greedy, but the punch was so good we QUAFFED glass after glass of it.	_____	_____
2. The doctor said the infant was CHOLERIC and had to be brought to the hospital immediately.	_____	_____
3. The DULCET sounds of a jackhammer kept him from getting any sleep.	_____	_____
4. The OBSEQUIOUS doorman took off his hat and bowed to us as we went in.	_____	_____
5. Jennifer REMUNERATED us that the party was Sunday night.	_____	_____
6. The TIMOROUS man always let other people get ahead of him in supermarket lines.	_____	_____
7. The CHURLISH ballplayer snarled at the boys asking for his autograph.	_____	_____
8. The traffic jam DILATED John for his appointment.	_____	_____
9. The president-elect chose his cabinet during the three-month HIATUS between winning the election and taking office.	_____	_____

10. They gave us extraordinary LASSITUDE, but we were still able to complete the job.   _____   _____

11. I'm not PETULANT; I just have high standards, and I get angry when people don't meet them.   _____   _____

12. In solemn REVERIE he begged God to forgive his sins.   _____   _____

13. If it hadn't been for your SAGACIOUS advice we would have made some very foolish mistakes.   _____   _____

14. The book's DIRE forecasts of coming wars and famines were very depressing.   _____   _____

15. Nothing could dampen their EBULLIENCE when the principal let them out of school early.   _____   _____

Exercise 3

Each test word is followed by three other words. Decide which of the three words is LEAST CLOSELY RELATED in its meaning to the meaning of the test word. Put the letter for the word you choose in the space at the end of the line.

EXAMPLE

TINY: **a)** small   **b)** short   **c)** angry   _C_

1. QUAFF: **a)** drink   **b)** dine   **c)** gulp   _____

2. CHOLERIC: **a)** pugnacious   **b)** frightened   **c)** peevish   _____

3. DULCET: **a)** harsh   **b)** tuneful   **c)** melodious   _____

4. OBSEQUIOUS: **a)** slavish   **b)** secretive   **c)** subservient   _____

5. REMUNERATE: **a)** recompense   **b)** rectify   **c)** reimburse   _____

6. TIMOROUS: **a)** frightened   **b)** vexing   **c)** daunted   _____

7. CHURLISH: **a)** brusque   **b)** dour   **c)** suspicious   _____

8. DILATE: **a)** expand   **b)** widen   **c)** shorten   _____

9. HIATUS: **a)** interval   **b)** conclusion   **c)** intermission   _____

10. LASSITUDE: **a)** depression   **b)** tiredness   **c)** listlessness   _____

11. PETULANT: **a)** irritable   **b)** sad   **c)** peevish   _____

12. REVERIE: **a)** thinking   **b)** planning   **c)** dreaming   _____

13. SAGACIOUS: **a)** holy   **b)** shrewd   **c)** wise   _____

14. DIRE: **a)** favorable   **b)** ominous   **c)** painful   _____

15. EBULLIENCE: **a)** exuberance   **b)** contentment   **c)** happiness   _____

Chapter 9

Pretest

Each test word is printed in CAPITAL letters. From the five choices on the next line, select the one which comes nearest in meaning to the meaning of the test word. Underline the one you select.

1. HAPLESS
   unhappy   useless   unlucky   vicious   stupid

2. to INCULCATE
   learn   demand   suggest   instill   lead to

3. INFINITESIMAL
   endless   tiny   essential   incredible   light

4. NOXIOUS
   explosive   dirty   powerful   sharp   harmful

5. PARSIMONIOUS
   formal   generous   stingy   sickly   tricky

6. POTABLE
   drinkable   edible   poisonous   valuable   powerful

7. VOCIFEROUS
   clamorous   impolite   vain   humorous   threatening

8. ABJECT
   real   impossible   frightened   wretched   drunken

9. BLITHE
   serious   weak   joyful   silly   lovely

10. CATARACT
    explosion   cliff   canyon   river   waterfall

11. to OBFUSCATE
    obscure   clarify   annoy   defeat   defile

12. OBSTREPEROUS
    obedient   precocious   determined   unruly   mean

13. to OSSIFY
    darken   rot   harden   soften   waver

14. to PORTEND
    resemble   forebode   cause   expect   recall

15. to PROTRACT
    prolong   produce   propose   plan   cancel

HAPLESS (hap'-ləs) adj.: unlucky, unfortunate

The *hap* part of HAPLESS comes from an archaic word related to the word *happen*. *Hap* once meant *chance* or *fortune*. Someone who is HAPLESS does not have good fortune; he is completely unlucky.

> "The HAPLESS woman broke her leg on the way home from the hospital."

> "The HAPLESS basketball team never seemed to get a break from the referees during its losing streak."

Useless is the most common wrong answer on the Pretest, perhaps because HAPLESS looks like *helpless* or *hopeless*.

INCULCATE (in-kəl'-kAt) v.: to instill, implant, teach earnestly

INCULCATE comes from a Latin word meaning to *trample in*. To INCULCATE something is to teach it or impress it upon someone by persistent repetitions, so that it becomes deeply implanted in his mind. The word is usually used with *in* or *into*.

> "It proved to be impossible to INCULCATE any sense of discipline into those boys."

> "The teacher tried to INCULCATE a love of language in her students."

> "From her earliest years, Deborah had been INCULCATED with a stern code of ethics."

INFINITESIMAL (in-fin-ə-tes'-ə-məl) adj.: tiny, minute, immeasurably small

INFINITESIMAL is related to the word *infinite*. The words, however, are almost completely opposite in meaning. *Infinite* means *endless*, "having no limits." INFINITESIMAL means "extremely minute, immeasurably small."

> "These INFINITESIMAL subatomic particles can be detected only by the most powerful electron microscopes."

The confusion between *infinite* and INFINITESIMAL illustrates the difficulty of figuring out a word's meaning by breaking it down into its parts, without seeing it in context. The person who is familiar with the contexts in which INFINITESIMAL is used would not be likely to think it means *endless*.

NOXIOUS (nok'-shəs) adj.: harmful, injurious, destructive, deleterious, detrimental

NOXIOUS and *obnoxious* both come from a Latin word meaning *harm* or *damage*. *Obnoxious* now simply means *offensive, disagreeable*. NOXIOUS is a stronger word, and keeps the original sense of actual harm. Something that is NOXIOUS is harmful to the body or the mind, to health or morals.

> "The NOXIOUS fumes of the chemical plant sent twenty people to the hospital."

> "Several studies have documented the NOXIOUS effects on children of watching too much television."

> "These NOXIOUS ideas have no place in our educational system."

PARSIMONIOUS (pahr-sə-mO'-nE-əs) adj.: stingy, niggardly

PARSIMONY is excessive thrift, extreme frugality. PARSIMONIOUS is the adjective from PARSIMONY; see *-ous* under Suffixes. PARSIMONIOUS and *stingy* are quite close in meaning, but there is a slight difference. *Stingy* suggests a mean-spirited unwillingness to share what one has. PARSIMONIOUS is not usually quite so negative; it would be used more of a person who carries the virtue of thrift or economy to extremes.

> "The rich man was so PARSIMONIOUS that he picked through other people's trash looking for clothing he might wear."

> "They accused Jill of being PARSIMONIOUS when she wouldn't buy a ticket to the concert, but she said thirty dollars was far too much to spend."

Generous, an opposite of PARSIMONIOUS, is the most common wrong answer on the Pretest item.

Other forms of the word: PARSIMONY, n.

POTABLE (pOt'-ə-bəl) adj.: drinkable, fit to drink

POTABLE means "fit to drink," *drinkable*. It is sometimes used as a noun and applied to beverages; they are referred to as POTABLES.

> "The army scout knew that the water in the algae-covered pond was not POTABLE."

> "My mother makes coffee so thick and bitter it is hardly POTABLE."

VOCIFEROUS (vO-sif'-ər-əs) adj.: clamorous, boisterous, strident

The *voc* part of VOCIFEROUS comes from the Latin word for *voice*, also the source of *vocal* and *advocate*. VOCIFEROUS people are always ready to use their voices, particularly to demand or object.

"The VOCIFEROUS fans at the boxing match let the fighters know they were displeased with the action."
"One VOCIFEROUS parent objected strongly to everything the principal said."
"Bowing to the children's VOCIFEROUS entreaties, their parents let them stay up to watch the special TV program."

ABJECT (ab'-jekt or ab-jekt') adj.: wretched, humiliating; contemptible, despicable

ABJECT means "extremely low in position, degree, or worth." Sometimes it has the sense of *wretched, hopeless*.

"They lived in ABJECT poverty, without a cent to their name."
"The ABJECT squalor of the apartment sickened us."

The word often has a negative or disparaging sense and means *contemptible*.

"The general's ABJECT cowardice was disgraceful."

BLITHE (blIth or blITH) adj.: joyful, glad, cheerful; carefree, casual, heedless

BLITHE means *joyful, merry, gay*. It suggests a lighthearted, carefree kind of joy, like that of a child.

"Nothing could upset the BLITHE young couple during the first months of their marriage."
"The BLITHE days of summer vacation were over, and now they had to face school once again."

BLITHE often puts the strongest emphasis on the carefree, heedless quality of this happiness, with the suggestion that this casualness may have bad consequences.

"The driver BLITHELY ignored their warning about the slippery roads."
"Her BLITHE refusal to worry about grades finally caused her to fail three courses."

CATARACT (kat'-ə-rakt) n.: a large waterfall, downpour, deluge

A CATARACT is a large waterfall or steep rapids.

"The canoeists came dangerously close to the CATARACT before they managed to reach shore."

CATARACT can also be used in an extended sense about any large downpour.

"CATARACTS of rain poured off the roof of our house during the storm."

OBFUSCATE (ob'-fuhs-kAt or ob'-fə-skAt) v.: to darken, make indistinct; to confuse, bewilder, make obscure

OBFUSCATE comes from a Latin word meaning to *darken*. The word can be used about actual physical darkness.

"The fog OBFUSCATED the land."

But it is generally used in a figurative sense, about intellectual darkness.

"If that journalist would write more clearly he would not OBFUSCATE his readers."

To OBFUSCATE something is to make it obscure, muddled, hard to understand.

"The court's contradictory rulings have served only to OBFUSCATE the new law."
"The inept writer managed to further OBFUSCATE an already unclear subject."

Other forms of the word: OBFUSCATION, n.
OBFUSCATORY, adj.

OBSTREPEROUS (ob-strep'-ər-əs) adj.: noisy, tumultuous, unruly, boisterous

OBSTREPEROUS is used about people who are noisily unruly, who are loud, aggressive, and difficult to control.

"The OBSTREPEROUS students were always causing a commotion in the classroom."
"Whenever people disagree with Bill he becomes OBSTREPEROUS."
"The judge ordered the OBSTREPEROUS spectators removed from the courtroom."

OSSIFY (os'-ə-fI) v.: to change into bone, harden

OSSIFY comes from the Latin word for *bone*. See -*fy* under Suffixes. OSSIFY means "to change or form into bone." In an extended sense, the word means "to mold or become set in a conventional pattern," to *harden* or *become rigid*.

"The elderly man rejected the notion that people's minds tend to OSSIFY as they get older."

"The passage of time had OSSIFIED both parties in their positions, so that compromise seemed unlikely."

"The organization's practices were so OSSIFIED that it was unable to adapt to change."

Other forms of the word: OSSIFICATION, n.

—————————————

PORTEND (pôr-tend') v.: to forebode, foreshadow

To PORTEND is to forbode or presage. PORTEND is usually applied to a coming evil or disaster. See PORTENT in Chapter 2.

"Geese flying south in October PORTEND an early and hard winter."

"Madame Zelda said the signs in the tea leaves PORTENDED misfortunes for the lady."

"The critic's bored sighs PORTEND a bad review."

Other forms of the word: PORTENT, n.
PORTENTOUS, adj.

—————————————

PROTRACT (prO-trakt') v.: to prolong, drag out

To PROTRACT means "to lengthen in duration," *prolong*. The word often implies that the prolonging is unnecessary or boring.

"They PROTRACTED the conference with an endless series of unnecessary speeches."

"The discussion between the two businessmen became so PROTRACTED that the other people at the meeting started to fall asleep."

"Stevens was so bored at work that he wrote a PROTRACTED memo on the virtues of unlined paper: it came to fifteen pages."

Exercise 1

Answer each question with a YES or NO. Put a check in the space for YES or NO next to each question.

		Yes	No
1.	Does a HAPLESS person have bad luck?	_____	_____
2.	Can you INCULCATE something by repetition?	_____	_____
3.	Are galaxies INFINITESIMAL?	_____	_____
4.	Can chemical fumes be NOXIOUS?	_____	_____
5.	Do PARSIMONIOUS people usually give expensive presents?	_____	_____
6.	Is sulfuric acid POTABLE?	_____	_____
7.	Are shy people usually VOCIFEROUS?	_____	_____
8.	Might a very poor person live in ABJECT poverty?	_____	_____
9.	Would a BLITHE person tend to worry a lot?	_____	_____
10.	Could Niagara Falls be called a CATARACT?	_____	_____
11.	Should politicians OBFUSCATE issues?	_____	_____
12.	Are OBSTREPEROUS people easily controlled?	_____	_____
13.	Is it easy to change something that has OSSIFIED?	_____	_____
14.	Do black clouds PORTEND a storm?	_____	_____
15.	Would people want to cut short a PROTRACTED discussion?	_____	_____

Exercise 2

Each sentence contains a test word in CAPITAL letters. Decide whether the test word is being used correctly or incorrectly in the sentence. Put a check in the space for RIGHT or WRONG next to the sentence.

		Right	Wrong
1.	Nothing went right for the HAPLESS settlers that first year.	_____	_____
2.	The stranger INCULCATED us the way to the fairgrounds.	_____	_____
3.	The human body needs only INFINITESIMAL amounts of some minerals.	_____	_____
4.	The government determined that the food additive was NOXIOUS.	_____	_____
5.	Fred PARSIMONIOUSLY agreed to help us on our research project.	_____	_____
6.	The Smiths were in charge of the food, and we were supposed to provide the POTABLES for the picnic.	_____	_____
7.	The players VOCIFEROUSLY protested the referee's call.	_____	_____
8.	Nancy's ABJECT unhappiness made us all feel sorry for her.	_____	_____
9.	His BLITHE disregard for the rules may force us to disqualify him.	_____	_____
10.	During the parade the crowd showered CATARACTS of confetti on the returning heroes.	_____	_____

11. The police OBFUSCATED us to leave the area immediately.   _____   _____

12. The OBSTREPEROUS drunk offered to fight anyone in the bar.   _____   _____

13. Angela OSSIFIED her ideas into something new and exciting.   _____   _____

14. The students PORTENDED that nothing bad would happen.   _____   _____

15. The company PROTRACTED with us to use our product.   _____   _____

Exercise 3

Each test word is followed by three other words. Decide which of the three words is LEAST CLOSELY RELATED in its meaning to the meaning of the test word. Put the letter for the word you choose in the space at the end of the line.

EXAMPLE

TINY: **a)** small   **b)** short   **c)** angry   __C__

1. HAPLESS: **a)** harmless   **b)** luckless   **c)** disastrous   _____

2. INCULCATE: **a)** tell   **b)** implant   **c)** instruct   _____

3. INFINITESIMAL: **a)** microscopic   **b)** minute   **c)** telescopic   _____

4. NOXIOUS: **a)** vapid   **b)** harmful   **c)** detrimental   _____

5. PARSIMONIOUS: **a)** nasty   **b)** miserly   **c)** greedy   _____

6. POTABLE: **a)** wine   **b)** water   **c)** mud   _____

7. VOCIFEROUS: **a)** docile   **b)** noisy   **c)** strident   _____

8. ABJECT: **a)** fierce   **b)** sordid   **c)** pitiful   _____

9. BLITHE: **a)** sagacious   **b)** ebullient   **c)** heedless   _____

10. CATARACT: **a)** cascade   **b)** ocean   **c)** torrent   _____

11. OBFUSCATE: **a)** perplex   **b)** daunt   **c)** befog   _____

12. OBSTREPEROUS: **a)** fretful   **b)** intractable   **c)** disorderly   _____

13. OSSIFY: **a)** harden   **b)** fossilize   **c)** grow   _____

14. PORTEND: **a)** forebode   **b)** prophesy   **c)** think   _____

15. PROTRACT: **a)** refine   **b)** amplify   **c)** extend   _____

Review Test 3—Chapters 7–9

Fill in each blank with the test word (or a form of the test word) which best fits the sentence. Use the words listed below.

ABJECT   FRETFUL   INFINITESIMAL   PARSIMONIOUS   REMUNERATE
CATACLYSM   HIATUS   MESMERIZE   PRODIGY   REVERIE
CHURLISH   IMBROGLIO   MISCREANT   PROTRACT   SAGACIOUS
DAUNT   INCULCATE   OBFUSCATE   QUAFF   TENET
DEMISE

1. Our parents tried to _____ in us a sense of responsibility for our actions.

2. The youthful _____ was found guilty of armed robbery, assault with a dangerous weapon, and car theft.

3. As a child John Stuart Mill was quite a(n) _____; he could speak Latin and Greek by the age of five.

4. Instead of clarifying the complex issue, her remarks served only to _____ it further.

5. Nothing _____ us; we were determined to succeed, and ultimately we did.

6. He tried to _____ his stay because he had no place else to live.

7. One of the _____ of this political party is: "the less government, the better."

8. In her quiet _____, dreams and images and memories floated through her mind.

9. The leader of the search party said that even if there was only a(n) _____ chance of finding any survivors, they would continue to look.

10. There was a(n) _____ of several years between the completion of the novel and its publication.

11. The _____ over who had the right to use the parking space soon involved everyone in the office.

12. The _____ salesclerk told them to hurry up and make up their minds.

13. There is no need to _____ us for our services; we are happy to donate them.

14. The _____ stockbroker knew from long experience exactly the right times to buy and sell.

15. He would sit for hours, _____ by the constantly shifting pattern of shadows on the wall.

16. They expected her to _____ the whole drink, but she only took one sip.

17. When Sally was overtired, she became _____ and would snap at everyone.

18. Even though he had plenty of money, the _____ man kept track of every nickel he spent.

19. Earthquakes, volcanic eruptions, and other _____ were seen as evidence of God's displeasure.

20. After the dictator's _____, his followers battled to determine who would succeed him.

21. The family lived in such _____ poverty they could not afford new clothing.

Fill in each blank with the test word (or a form of the test word) which best fits the sentence. Use the words listed below.

AMBIENCE   DIRE   HAPLESS   OBSTREPEROUS   POTABLE
BLITHE   DOLOROUS   HINTERLAND   OSSIFY   PROGENY
CATARACT   DULCET   LASSITUDE   PEEVISH   TIMOROUS
CHOLERIC   EBULLIENCE NOXIOUS   PETULANT   VOCIFEROUS
DILATE   FLACCID   OBSEQUIOUS   PORTEND

22. George Washington had no children of his own, but in a sense all Americans can be considered his

    _____.

23. The hotel tried to create a romantic _____ for the many newlyweds who stayed there.

24. His problems during the first day of vacation _____ a disagreeable two weeks.

25. Over the years his mind has _____, and he never has any new ideas.

26. When Jill saw how _____ her body had become, she decided it was time to do some serious exercising.

27. We listened to Sam's _____ tale about all the misfortunes that had befallen him.

28. The _____ child cried and complained whenever he didn't get his own way.

29. The wine was bitter but _____; we managed to finish the bottle.

30. The _____ lady complained constantly about everything.

31. The _____ audience started shouting and demanding their money back when the film projector broke.

32. Her _____, sunny disposition made it seem as if she didn't have a problem in the world.

33. We listened with pleasure to the _____ sounds of the mother crooning a lullaby to her baby.

34. The sudden hundred-foot drop turned the peaceful river into a dangerous _____.

35. Sarah was so _____ that she was afraid to complain when the waitress brought her the wrong order.

36. The _____ gas leaking from the chemical factory caused authorities to evacuate the area.

37. The _____ man would explode with anger at the slightest provocation.

38. The _____ spectators became so loud and unruly that the quarterback couldn't be heard by his team.

39. The Red Cross said there was a(n) _____ need for medical supplies in the flood-stricken area.

40. Alan tried to restrain his _____, but we could tell how excited he was by the news.

41. The _____ young man had more than his share of bad luck this year.

42. After all our frenzied activity we fell into a state of _____ that lasted for weeks.

43. The _____ waiter was always at our side, inquiring if there were anything he could do for us.

44. In dim light, the pupil of the eye _____, letting in as much light as possible.

45. After living in the _____ all his life, the young man was overwhelmed by the fast pace of the city.

Chapter 10

Pretest

Each test word is printed in CAPITAL letters. From the five choices on the next line, select the one which comes nearest in meaning to the meaning of the test word. Underline the one you select.

1. ANCILLARY
       prior   auxiliary   official   unknown   ineffective

2. to BELIE
       support   resemble   delay   contradict   lessen

3. INIQUITOUS
       sinless   nervous   wicked   secret   incredible

4. PROPINQUITY
       support   evil   distance   oddity   nearness

5. TENABLE
       defensible   hazardous   valuable   limited   noticeable

6. ASSIDUOUS
       courteous   helpful   treacherous   lazy   diligent

7. to ESCHEW
       desire   shun   separate   consider   dislike

8. PERFIDY
       excellence   similarity   loyalty   treachery   slander

9. PRODIGIOUS
       nasty   favorable   huge   complicated   disappointing

10. SINUOUS
        curving   knowing   long   tempting   beautiful

11. UBIQUITOUS
        invisible   omnipresent   evil   all-knowing   immense

12. to APPRISE
        commend   improve   deceive   notice   inform

13. EXPIATION
        atonement   guilt   alibi   discussion   admission

14. EXTANT
        existing   obsolete   eminent   overjoyed   uncaptured

15. FATUOUS
        dangerous   idealistic   foolish   disgusting   talkative

ANCILLARY (an'-sə-ler-E) adj.: auxiliary, secondary, subordinate, subsidiary

ANCILLARY comes from a Latin word meaning *maid-servant,* and means "giving help or support from a subordinate position."

"The police department, with its ANCILLARY citizen patrols, was able to halt the rise of crime."
"A good teacher often has the ANCILLARY attributes of patience and a sense of humor."

Sometimes ANCILLARY loses this sense of support or aid, and merely means *secondary* or *supplementary.*

"Chris majored in Russian literature, but also took ANCILLARY subjects like European history and philosophy."

BELIE (bi-lI') v.: to contradict, prove false

BELIE, which is related to the word *lie,* means to "give the lie" to something. The word is usually used in situations where one's words are contradicted by one's appearance, or where one's actions contradict one's words.

"His confident speech BELIED his apprehension."
"His continued association with known criminals BELIED his promises to reform."

In a slightly different sense, BELIE can mean to *disguise* or *misrepresent.*

"His suave behavior BELIED his humble origins."

INIQUITOUS (i-nik'-wə-təs) adj.: wicked, sinful, villainous

INIQUITOUS comes from a Latin word meaning *unjust.* See *in-₂* under Prefixes and *-ous* under Suffixes. In English, INIQUITOUS has a much stronger meaning than simply *unjust.* It suggests a total absence of fairness and principles, an evil disregard of justice.

"The murderer expressed no repentance for his INIQUITOUS crimes."
"The INIQUITOUS king ordered all his opponents beheaded."

Other forms of the word: INIQUITY, n.

PROPINQUITY (prə-ping'-kwi-tE) n.: nearness, proximity

PROPINQUITY means *nearness.* Originally PROPINQUITY referred only to nearness of blood or relationship, *kinship.* Now the word is used about any kind of nearness.

"The inn's PROPINQUITY to the sea makes it a delightful summer resort."
"The PROPINQUITY of the two events made us think that one had caused the other."

TENABLE (ten'-ə-bəl) adj.: defensible, reasonable

TENABLE comes from a Latin word meaning to *hold,* also the source of TENACIOUS. Something that is TENABLE is able to be held or defended.

"When their position was no longer TENABLE the troops were forced to retreat."

Similarly, the word is used about intellectual positions that can be defended.

"The astronomer's theory about the origin of the solar system seemed TENABLE."

The opposite of TENABLE, UNTENABLE, is frequently used.

"Scientists dismissed his arguments as UNTENABLE in the light of new evidence."

Other forms of the word: UNTENABLE, adj.

ASSIDUOUS (ə-sij'-U-əs) adj.: diligent, devoted, constant, sedulous

ASSIDUOUS means *constant* or *diligent* in carrying out a task or doing one's duty. The word is used of people who keep their energy and attention focused on a particular task.

"The ASSIDUOUS servant made sure everything was in order for his master's return."
"Through ASSIDUOUS studying Amy managed to graduate at the top of her class."
"Harold tried ASSIDUOUSLY to learn how to play the piano, practicing four or five hours a day."

Other forms of the word: ASSIDUITY, n.

ESCHEW (is-chU′) v.: to shun, abstain from, forgo, avoid

To ESCHEW something is to avoid or shun it, usually because it would be immoral, unwise, or harmful.

"The doctor advised him to ESCHEW alcohol and tobacco if he wanted to recover."

"Hemingway ESCHEWED the use of overblown figures of speech in his novels."

"Vegetarians ESCHEW meat."

Other forms of the word: ESCHEWAL, n.

PERFIDY (per′-fi-dE) n.: treachery, faithlessness

PERFIDY is deliberate breach of faith, *treachery*. It is a strong word and implies great contempt.

"We can never forgive his PERFIDY; we trusted him, and he betrayed us."

"Benedict Arnold's name has become synonymous with PERFIDY."

A PERFIDY is also an act of treachery.

"The traitor's PERFIDIES are so numerous we can't list them all."

The adjective PERFIDIOUS means *traitorous, faithless*.

"Cressida was a PERFIDIOUS lover; after she promised to be faithful to Troilus, she deserted him for the Greek Diomedes."

Other forms of the word: PERFIDIOUS, adj.

PRODIGIOUS (prə-dij′-əs) adj.: huge, enormous, tremendous, stupendous

A PRODIGY is a wonder, a marvel, particularly an exceptionally gifted person. See the discussion of PRODIGY in Chapter 7. PRODIGIOUS is the adjective from PRODIGY. See *-ous* under Suffixes. PRODIGIOUS usually emphasizes something's amazing size, capacity, or the like.

"His PRODIGIOUS memory enabled him to recall anything he had ever read."

"She had a PRODIGIOUS appetite. She never seemed to have enough to eat."

"The PRODIGIOUS size of the federal deficit forced Congress to raise taxes."

Favorable is by far the most common wrong answer on the Pretest. This may be due to a confusion with the word *auspicious*. Or it may have something to do with the original meaning of PRODIGY, a *sign* or *omen*, which might suggest *favorable*. PRODIGIOUS once meant *portentous, ominous*, but this meaning is now obsolete.

Other forms of the word: PRODIGY, n.

SINUOUS (sin′-yU-əs) adj.: curving, winding

SINUOUS comes from the Latin word for a curve. The word means "full of curves," *winding*.

"The SINUOUS path of the road makes it very treacherous."

SINUOUS often suggests suppleness and smoothness of movement.

"The SINUOUS movements of the dancers entranced the audience."

The *sin* part of SINUOUS perhaps leads people to choose *tempting*, which is the most commonly chosen wrong answer in the Pretest item.

UBIQUITOUS (yU-bik′-wi-təs) adj.: omnipresent, existing everywhere at once

UBIQUITOUS means "existing, or seeming to exist, everywhere at the same time." It is usually used in a somewhat exaggerated sense about people or things that one always seems to be encountering.

"In the hotel we found it impossible to avoid the UBIQUITOUS conventioneers."

"The UBIQUITOUS pigeon can be found in every city."

"In the early summer dandelions seem to be UBIQUITOUS; every lawn is filled with them."

Other forms of the word: UBIQUITY, n.

APPRISE (ə-prIz′) v.: to inform, notify, cause to know

To APPRISE people of something is to give them notice of it, to cause them to know it.

> "The president APPRISED his advisers of the situation and asked for their opinion."
> "Rich APPRISED us that he was resigning effective the fifteenth of April."
> "I wish you would APPRISE me of your intentions. I hate being kept in suspense."

EXPIATION (ek-spE-A′-shən) n.: atonement, amends, reparation

To EXPIATE a crime or a sin is to make up for it by doing penance or by making amends.

> "You cannot EXPIATE your offense simply by saying it was all a mistake."

EXPIATION is the noun from EXPIATE. It is the act of EXPIATING.

> "His sin was so great that the EXPIATION of it would not be easy."

EXPIATION is also the means of making atonement.

> "The gang member offered the victim a large sum of money as partial EXPIATION for his part in the crime."

Other forms of the word: EXPIATE, v.
EXPIATORY, adj.

EXTANT (ek′-stənt or ek-stant′) adj.: still existing, not lost or destroyed

EXTANT means "still in existence; not lost, destroyed, or exterminated."

> "There are several different species of this fish EXTANT in the Caribbean."

The context often suggests that the things which are EXTANT are relatively rare—that most similar things do *not* still exist.

> "The three EXTANT photographs of the man all show him with red hair."
> "There is only one copy of the first edition of Shakespeare's play *Titus Andronicus* EXTANT. It is in the Folger Library in Washington."

The most popular wrong answer is *obsolete*, which is virtually an opposite of EXTANT.

FATUOUS (fach′-U-əs) adj.: foolish, inane, silly

FATUOUS means *stupid, silly*. The word usually suggests a complacent, unwitting foolishness, and is used contemptuously.

> "After a while no one at the meeting paid any attention to Gail's FATUOUS statements."
> "These FATUOUS situation comedies are an insult to my intelligence."
> "She is a foolish woman, always making FATUOUS remarks."

Other forms of the word: FATUITY, n.

Exercise 1

Answer each question with a YES or NO. Put a check in the space for YES or NO next to each question.

	Yes	No
1. Is ANCILLARY equipment crucial to a job?	———	———
2. Would rude behavior BELIE a dignified manner?	———	———
3. Is jaywalking INIQUITOUS?	———	———
4. Can events occur in close PROPINQUITY to each other?	———	———
5. Are TENABLE views always correct?	———	———
6. Do ASSIDUOUS workers sleep on the job?	———	———
7. Would a stingy person ESCHEW spending money?	———	———
8. Is PERFIDY considered wicked?	———	———
9. Would running a mile in three minutes be a PRODIGIOUS feat?	———	———
10. Can the path of a river be SINUOUS?	———	———
11. Is ice UBIQUITOUS in Antarctica?	———	———
12. Does a report card APPRISE parents of how their child is doing in school?	———	———
13. Can a public apology for a misdeed be considered a form of EXPIATION?	———	———
14. Are dinosaurs EXTANT?	———	———
15. Would a wise person usually make FATUOUS remarks?	———	———

Exercise 2

Each sentence contains a test word in CAPITAL letters. Decide whether the test word is being used correctly or incorrectly in the sentence. Put a check in the space for RIGHT or WRONG next to the sentence.

	Right	Wrong
1. For this course, there is one required textbook and an ANCILLARY reading list.	———	———
2. Her warm smile BELIED her usually unpleasant manner.	———	———
3. The prosecutor demanded the death penalty for the INIQUITOUS criminal.	———	———
4. The PROPINQUITY of our goal made it all the more frustrating for us when we couldn't reach it.	———	———
5. The current state of the economy makes her position on the tax cut no longer TENABLE.	———	———
6. Because of Bill's ASSIDUOUS attention to detail, he uncovered several small mistakes in the report.	———	———
7. The movement ESCHEWED violence as a means of achieving its goals.	———	———
8. The Soviet government attacked the PERFIDY of the defector.	———	———
9. Finding ten dollars on the sidewalk was certainly a PRODIGIOUS start for the day.	———	———

10. His SINUOUS conduct offended us all. _____ _____

11. Henry was so UBIQUITOUS he figured he wouldn't even bother going to school. _____ _____

12. The principal APPRISED the students for winning the debating championship. _____ _____

13. An ancient way of EXPIATING one's sins was to wear sackcloth and ashes. _____ _____

14. Copies of Gutenberg's Bible, the first important book printed with movable type, are EXTANT. _____ _____

15. Too many rich desserts had made her rather FATUOUS. _____ _____

Exercise 3

Each test word is followed by three other words. Decide which of the three words is LEAST CLOSELY RELATED in its meaning to the meaning of the test word. Put the letter for the word you choose in the space at the end of the line.

EXAMPLE

    TINY: **a)** small   **b)** short   **c)** angry   _C_

1. ANCILLARY: **a)** revised   **b)** supplemented   **c)** assisted   _____

2. BELIE: **a)** confuse   **b)** refute   **c)** disprove   _____

3. INIQUITOUS: **a)** sinful   **b)** criminal   **c)** mistaken   _____

4. PROPINQUITY: **a)** nearness   **b)** relationship   **c)** vagueness   _____

5. TENABLE: **a)** unassailable   **b)** understandable   **c)** reasonable   _____

6. ASSIDUOUS: **a)** industrious   **b)** indolent   **c)** untiring   _____

7. ESCHEW: **a)** forgo   **b)** abstain   **c)** anticipate   _____

8. PERFIDY: **a)** faithlessness   **b)** disorderliness   **c)** treachery   _____

9. PRODIGIOUS: **a)** mammoth   **b)** marvelous   **c)** minute   _____

10. SINUOUS: **a)** tortuous   **b)** dangerous   **c)** supple   _____

11. UBIQUITOUS: **a)** everywhere   **b)** commonplace   **c)** occasional   _____

12. APPRISE: **a)** tell   **b)** ask   **c)** notify   _____

13. EXPIATION: **a)** reward   **b)** repayment   **c)** rectification   _____

14. EXTANT: **a)** present   **b)** extinct   **c)** living   _____

15. FATUOUS: **a)** inane   **b)** piercing   **c)** asinine   _____

Chapter 11

Pretest

Each test word is printed in CAPITAL letters. From the five choices on the next line, select the one which comes nearest in meaning to the meaning of the test word. Underline the one you select.

1. to INCOMMODE
   order   disturb   ignore   hurt   assist

2. INCREDULOUS
   skeptical   naive   terrified   uncertain   extraordinary

3. INVECTIVE
   stimulus   teaching   passion   abuse   illness

4. ONEROUS
   burdensome   illustrious   monotonous   ordinary   dangerous

5. PROPITIOUS
   wrong   uncertain   favorable   necessary   formal

6. to RUMINATE
   evaluate   rejoice   sleep   wander   meditate

7. to ADMONISH
   praise   warn   surprise   disapprove   torture

8. HIRSUTE
   hairy   smooth   ugly   hot   graceful

9. IGNOMINIOUS
   triumphant   humiliating   illiterate   counterfeit   threatening

10. IMPLACABLE
    faultless   unjustified   relentless   unlikely   unique

11. VOLUBLE
    famous   typical   humorous   talkative   noisy

12. ANOMALY
    version   proof   axiom   example   irregularity

13. FERAL
    soft   wild   masculine   ancient   frightening

14. PAROXYSM
    symptom   laughter   spasm   ache   gasp

15. TRIBULATION
    rejoicing   hard work   deep thought   loneliness   suffering

INCOMMODE (in-kə-mOd′) v.: to disturb, inconvenience, trouble

To INCOMMODE people is to put them to some inconvenience, to cause a problem with their plans or to interfere with their comfort.

> "Sharon insisted she was not INCOMMODED by our sudden change in plans."
> "The pilot said he was sorry to INCOMMODE us, but we would all have to get off the plane while the engine was being fixed."

The similar word *discommode* has essentially the same meaning.

INCREDULOUS (in-krej′-ə-ləs) adj.: skeptical, disinclined to believe

Credere is the Latin verb for *believe*. From this comes the English word *credulous*, meaning "inclined to believe." INCREDULOUS is the combination of *credulous* plus the prefix *in-*, meaning *not*. Thus INCREDULOUS means "not inclined to believe," *skeptical*.

> "In the 1400s, many people were INCREDULOUS when they were told that the world was round."
> "His wife's INCREDULOUS expression told George that she didn't believe his excuse."

The most commonly chosen wrong answer on the Pretest is *extraordinary*, probably because of a confusion with *incredible. Incredible*, with the same root as INCREDULOUS, literally means "unbelievable," but the word is often applied to extraordinary things. INCREDULOUS, however, means *skeptical*.

INVECTIVE (in-vek′-tiv) n.: abuse, vituperation

INVECTIVE is abusive language or an abusive, insulting expression. The word usually suggests some skill or cleverness in the insults, and they are often for a good cause.

> "Alexander Pope was a master of INVECTIVE; his enemies often felt the sting of his witty insults."

> "The politician was stung by the fury of his opponent's INVECTIVE."

The most commonly chosen wrong answer is *stimulus*, which is probably due to a misreading of *incentive* for INVECTIVE.

ONEROUS (on′-ər-əs or O′-nər-əs) adj.: burdensome, troublesome, oppressive

ONEROUS comes from the Latin word for *burden*. See *-ous* under Suffixes. ONEROUS is a close synonym of *burdensome*. It often stresses the distastefulness of the burden, and often applies to nonphysical kinds of burdens.

> "Bill's boss gave him the ONEROUS task of moving hundreds of heavy crates."
> "The Senator claimed that the new taxes were too ONEROUS and would have to be cut."
> "It really was not a very ONEROUS job. All she had to do was sit at a desk and answer the phone once or twice a day."

Dangerous is the most commonly chosen wrong answer on the Pretest, perhaps because of confusion with *ominous*.

PROPITIOUS (prə-pish′-əs) adj.: favorable, auspicious, encouraging; benevolent, kindly

PROPITIOUS means "presenting favorable circumstances." Like the similar word *auspicious* (see Chapter 4), PROPITIOUS comes from the ancient practice of looking for omens to see if the gods were in favor of a particular enterprise.

> "The meeting between the two world leaders had a PROPITIOUS start: they agreed immediately on the agenda."
> "John thought that circumstances were PROPITIOUS for asking the teacher to cancel the class."

The word is also used about people or things that are favorably disposed toward something.

> "If the gods are PROPITIOUS then all will turn out well."

Other forms of the word: PROPITIATE, v.
PROPITIATION, n.

RUMINATE (rU′-mə-nAt) v.: to meditate, muse, ponder

RUMINATE comes from a Latin word that means to *chew cud*. RUMINANTS are cattle, sheep, goats, and other animals that chew cud, which is partially digested food. Although RUMINATE can still mean to *chew cud*, it is now usually used in the figurative sense of "chewing things over" mentally, and means "to muse at length, to ponder over and over," like a cow chewing its cud. It is usually followed by *on*.

> "The engineer RUMINATED on the problem overnight, and by morning she had the solution."
> "The philosopher loved to RUMINATE on the mysteries of life."
> "Stanley spent so much time RUMINATING on the question that he never got around to answering it."

Other forms of the word: RUMINANT, n.
　　　　　　　　　　　RUMINATION, n.
　　　　　　　　　　　RUMINATIVE, adj.

ADMONISH (ad-mon′-ish) v.: to warn, reprove, rebuke

To ADMONISH is to warn or advise against something.

> "The babysitter ADMONISHED the children not to talk when they should be sleeping."

In a slightly different sense, to ADMONISH is to reprove or to scold, especially in a kindly but earnest way.

> "The teacher ADMONISHED the children for not paying attention."
> "When gently ADMONISHING her children didn't work, the mother threatened to punish them."

Disapprove is the most common wrong answer, probably because you would disapprove of people's conduct when you ADMONISH them. The two words are not synonymous, however.

Other forms of the word: ADMONISHMENT, n.
　　　　　　　　　　　ADMONITION, n.
　　　　　　　　　　　ADMONITORY, adj.

HIRSUTE (her′-sUt or her-sUt′) adj.: hairy, shaggy

HIRSUTE means "covered with hair," *shaggy*.

> "The large, HIRSUTE dog left little clumps of fur all over the carpet."
> "Mr. Jones ordered his HIRSUTE son to get a haircut."

IGNOMINIOUS (ig-nO-min′-E-əs) adj.: humiliating, disgraceful

The *nomin* part of IGNOMINIOUS comes from a Latin word meaning *name* or *reputation*. The prefix *ig-* is a variant of *in-*, meaning *not*. See *-ous* under Suffixes. Something that is IGNOMINIOUS would cause the loss of one's reputation; it is utterly disgraceful.

> "The once-proud man suffered an IGNOMINIOUS fate."
> "The football team's latest defeat was the most IGNOMINIOUS of all; they lost by seventy points."

The noun related to IGNOMINIOUS is IGNOMINY, which means *disgrace, great shame*.

> "He had to endure the IGNOMINY of working for the same person he had once tried to fire."

Other forms of the word: IGNOMINY, n.

IMPLACABLE (im-plak′-ə-bəl) adj.: relentless, inexorable, unappeasable

The *plac* part of IMPLACABLE comes from the Latin word meaning to *please*. The root meaning of IMPLACABLE is "not able to be pleased." See *in-₂* under Prefixes and *-able* under Suffixes. The word is used about people who cannot be appeased or pacified and about things that cannot be changed.

> "The IMPLACABLE enemy turned down all offers of compromise."
> "He was fascinated by the IMPLACABLE movement of the planets around the sun."

Other forms of the word: IMPLACABILITY, n.

VOLUBLE (vol'-yə-bəl) adj.: talkative, wordy, loquacious, garrulous

VOLUBLE comes originally from the Latin word *volvere*, to *turn*, also the source of the English word *revolve*. VOLUBLE originally meant "easy to turn," but it now has a very different meaning: *talkative, loquacious*. The image is of a rapidly moving tongue, one that produces an almost unstoppable stream of words. The word is usually used in a mildly derogatory sense.

> "She is so VOLUBLE that it is impossible to get a word in edgewise."
> "His VOLUBLE answers to simple questions began to bore us."

The most popular wrong answer is *noisy*. People who choose *noisy* perhaps think that VOLUBLE has something to do with *volume*. VOLUBLE has to do with how long people talk, not how loud they are.

Other forms of the word: VOLUBILITY, n.

ANOMALY (ə-nom'-ə-lE) n.: a deviation, irregularity, abnormality, inconsistency

An ANOMALY is something that isn't what it should be—something that deviates from what is normal or what is believed.

> "A family without a telephone is an ANOMALY in the United States."
> "The discovery of several ANOMALIES led scientists to revise their theory of how continents were formed."

The adjective from ANOMALY is ANOMALOUS, which means *abnormal, irregular*.

> "The intellectual goalie was an ANOMALOUS figure in professional hockey."

Other forms of the word: ANOMALOUS, adj.

FERAL (fEr'-əl or fer'-əl) adj.: wild, savage, brutal

FERAL means "having the characteristics of a wild animal." The word usually emphasizes the savagery and ferocity of such creatures, but can be applied to other characteristics as well.

> "The FERAL shrieks of the natives filled us with terror."
> "The man stalked his victim with FERAL cunning."

FERAL is also used to refer to wild animals generally, as opposed to tame or domesticated animals. It is often applied to animals that return to a state of wildness after having been tame.

> "Some dogs escaped into the woods and reverted to a FERAL state."

PAROXYSM (par'-ək-siz-əm) n.: a spasm, convulsion, sudden outburst

In medicine, a PAROXYSM is a sudden intensification of a disease or one of its symptoms, usually happening periodically.

> "She seemed better for a while, and then had another PAROXYSM of coughing."

In general use, PAROXYSM is applied to any sudden uncontrollable outburst of emotion or violent action.

> "Mary's sudden PAROXYSM of rage shocked everyone into silence."

TRIBULATION (trib-yə-lA'-shən) n.: suffering, affliction, hardship, trial

TRIBULATION is great distress or suffering. It is also an example or instance of this suffering.

> "They suffered great TRIBULATIONS during the war."
> "The former prisoners of war could not bear to discuss the TRIBULATIONS they had undergone."

TRIBULATIONS is often used in the phrase "trials and TRIBULATIONS." *Trial* in this sense has essentially the same meaning as TRIBULATION. *Rejoicing* is the most common wrong answer on the Pretest, probably because of confusion with the word *jubilation*.

Exercise 1

Answer each question with a YES or NO. Put a check in the space for YES or NO next to each question.

		Yes	No
1.	Would a noisy hotel guest INCOMMODE other guests?	_____	_____
2.	Are there INCREDULOUS people?	_____	_____
3.	Would it be INVECTIVE to call someone a "miserable cur"?	_____	_____
4.	Is an ONEROUS task likely to bother a person?	_____	_____
5.	Would a touchdown on the first play be a PROPITIOUS start for a football team?	_____	_____
6.	Is a snap decision the result of RUMINATING?	_____	_____
7.	Would a teacher ADMONISH a student for being diligent?	_____	_____
8.	Is an ape HIRSUTE?	_____	_____
9.	Is it IGNOMINIOUS to be intelligent?	_____	_____
10.	Is it easy to defeat an IMPLACABLE enemy?	_____	_____
11.	Are salesmen usually VOLUBLE?	_____	_____
12.	Would a restaurant that charged fifty cents for a steak dinner be considered an ANOMALY?	_____	_____
13.	Would most people find FERAL sounds comforting?	_____	_____
14.	Is a PAROXYSM usually pleasant?	_____	_____
15.	Are TRIBULATIONS hard to bear?	_____	_____

Exercise 2

Each sentence contains a test word in CAPITAL letters. Decide whether the test word is being used correctly or incorrectly in the sentence. Put a check in the space for RIGHT or WRONG next to the sentence.

		Right	Wrong
1.	The manager INCOMMODED them from the room a day early.	_____	_____
2.	With an INCREDULOUS effort he actually lifted the car off the ground.	_____	_____
3.	Far from praising the play, the review was full of INVECTIVES aimed at everyone in the cast.	_____	_____
4.	There were several ONEROUS signs that the house might be haunted.	_____	_____
5.	The meeting began PROPITIOUSLY when everyone arrived on time, but ended in chaos when no one could agree on anything.	_____	_____
6.	The teacher RUMINATED us that the principal might resign soon.	_____	_____
7.	Mr. Mulligan was ADMONISHED of his daughter staying out all night.	_____	_____
8.	I wish he weren't bald; I prefer men who are more HIRSUTE.	_____	_____
9.	Their IGNOMINIOUS antics delighted everyone in the audience.	_____	_____

71

10. The residents were IMPLACABLY opposed to a new skyscraper being built in their neighborhood.   —————   —————

11. The stereo was so VOLUBLE that we couldn't hear ourselves think.   —————   —————

12. The ANOMALOUS caller told the police where they could find the stolen money.   —————   —————

13. The people from the city were not used to the FERAL howls of the coyotes.   —————   —————

14. Despite an occasional PAROXYSM of fear he withstood his ordeal quite well.   —————   —————

15. There was great TRIBULATION in the city over the general's victory.   —————   —————

Exercise 3

Each test word is followed by three other words. Decide which of the three words is LEAST CLOSELY RELATED in its meaning to the meaning of the test word. Put the letter for the word you choose in the space at the end of the line.

EXAMPLE

	TINY:	a)	small	b)	short	c)	angry	C
1.	INCOMMODE:	a)	trouble	b)	burden	c)	pacify	—————
2.	INCREDULOUS:	a)	dubious	b)	daring	c)	skeptical	—————
3.	INVECTIVE:	a)	denial	b)	abuse	c)	insult	—————
4.	ONEROUS:	a)	heavy	b)	loose	c)	hard	—————
5.	PROPITIOUS:	a)	lovely	b)	kindly	c)	encouraging	—————
6.	RUMINATE:	a)	speak	b)	cogitate	c)	ponder	—————
7.	ADMONISH:	a)	chide	b)	debase	c)	upbraid	—————
8.	HIRSUTE:	a)	hairy	b)	scaly	c)	furry	—————
9.	IGNOMINIOUS:	a)	disgraceful	b)	degrading	c)	insubordinate	—————
10.	IMPLACABLE:	a)	solemn	b)	inflexible	c)	merciless	—————
11.	VOLUBLE:	a)	opinionated	b)	verbose	c)	garrulous	—————
12.	ANOMALY:	a)	problem	b)	deviation	c)	eccentricity	—————
13.	FERAL:	a)	wild	b)	fierce	c)	playful	—————
14.	PAROXYSM:	a)	disease	b)	fit	c)	outburst	—————
15.	TRIBULATION:	a)	distress	b)	trial	c)	danger	—————

Chapter 12

Pretest

Each test word is printed in CAPITAL letters. From the five choices on the next line, select the one which comes nearest in meaning to the meaning of the test word. Underline the one you select.

1. to VILIFY
   slander   appease   despise   terrify   cheat
2. ABNEGATION
   improvement   cancellation   self-denial   indulgence   purity
3. AMENABLE
   happy   submissive   irresponsible holy   fragile
4. ASCETIC
   holy   self-indulgent beautiful   austere   powerful
5. BELLICOSE
   warlike   peaceful   comical   overweight   evil
6. BENIGN
   kindly   lovely   silent   malicious   unforgiving
7. CREDULOUS
   stupid   unknown   extravagant   suspicious   gullible
8. PARADIGM
   story   model   lesson   copy   result
9. to SEQUESTER
   isolate   assemble   harass   protect   follow
10. STODGY
    lively   old   cruel   dull   clever
11. to SUFFUSE
    disappear   undergo   overspread   affect   darken
12. CELERITY
    rashness   swiftness   sluggishness   isolation   smoothness
13. ABLUTION
    staining   forgiveness   cleansing   prayer   blessing
14. to ABRADE
    insult   uproot   break apart   twist   wear away
15. ABSTRUSE
    mysterious   obvious   dull   forgotten   religious

73

VILIFY (vil′-ə-fI) v.: to slander, defame, malign

To VILIFY people is to speak ill of them with the intention of ruining their reputations, and without regard for the truth. The word suggests direct and violent accusation.

> "The newspaper had VILIFIED the accused murderer with such lurid stories that he couldn't get a fair trial."

> "The politician VILIFIED his opponent in the debate, calling him a thief and a scoundrel."

> "The manager should not be VILIFIED for her unorthodox methods."

Other forms of the word: VILIFICATION, n.

ABNEGATION (ab-ni-gA′-shən) n.: self-denial, renunciation, eschewal

The Latin word *negare* means to *deny,* to *say no.* It is the source of English words like *negate, negative,* and ABNEGATION. See *ab-* under Prefixes. ABNEGATION is self-denial, the practice of giving up what one desires. The term SELF-ABNEGATION is also frequently used, with the same meaning.

> "In an act of utter ABNEGATION, Joan said her sister should keep all of the inheritance."

> "We admire your ABNEGATION, but you must act in your own self-interest *once* in a while."

> "Through SELF-ABNEGATION he felt he was able to achieve a purity of spirit."

Other forms of the word: ABNEGATE, v.

AMENABLE (ə-mEn′-ə-bəl or ə-men′-ə-bəl) adj.: submissive, obedient, responsive; responsible

AMENABLE has two different meanings. One meaning is *submissive, responsive.* In this sense the word would be used about a person or thing that is naturally receptive to change, criticism, or the like. The word is often followed by *to.*

> "The teacher was quite AMENABLE to the idea of holding the class outdoors."

> "This problem is not AMENABLE to the kinds of solutions we have tried in the past."

The other meaning of AMENABLE is *accountable, responsible.*

> "The court ruled that he was AMENABLE for this debt."

The most common wrong answer on the Pretest is *happy,* perhaps suggested by the good-natured willingness of a person who is AMENABLE.

Other forms of the word: AMENABILITY, n.

ASCETIC (ə-set′-ik) adj.: austere, self-denying

ASCETIC is both an adjective and a noun. An ASCETIC is a person who leads an austere and self-disciplined life, fasting and avoiding the comforts of society, usually for religious reasons.

> "A small group of ASCETICS lived in the desert and spent their days in fasting and prayer."

As an adjective ASCETIC means "characteristic of an ASCETIC," *austere.*

> "Few people were strong enough to endure the monk's ASCETIC way of life."

> "The ASCETIC man denied himself all pleasures, saying he was atoning for his sins."

Beautiful is the most commonly chosen wrong answer on the Pretest. This is probably due to a confusion of ASCETIC with *aesthetic,* which means "pertaining to the sense of beauty," *artistic.*

Other forms of the word: ASCETICISM, n.

BELLICOSE (bel′-i-kOs) adj.: belligerent, warlike, combative

BELLICOSE, like the similar word *belligerent,* comes from the Latin *bellum,* meaning *war.* BELLICOSE means "having a warlike manner or attitude." It is often used in a somewhat weaker sense about people who are always ready to start an argument or pick a fight.

> "The BELLICOSE tribe was always at war."

> "The BELLICOSE drunk threatened to punch me in the nose."

The most commonly chosen wrong answer on the Pretest is *comical,* perhaps because of confusion with *jocose,* which means *merry, humorous.*

Other forms of the word: BELLICOSITY, n.

BENIGN (bi-nIn') adj.: kindly, gracious; favorable

BENIGN comes from the Latin word *bene,* meaning *well,* also the source of the English words *benevolent* and *beneficial.* BENIGN has two related meanings. The first is "having a kind or gentle temperament."

"The BENIGN man simply smiled and put down his book when the children interrupted his reading."

"You certainly could not say that Adolf Hitler, the leader of Nazi Germany, was a BENIGN ruler."

The other meaning is *favorable, beneficial.*

"The older boy's good example had a BENIGN influence on the younger children."

In medicine, a BENIGN tumor is one that doesn't threaten one's health or life. In this sense, the opposite of BENIGN is *malignant.*

By far the most popular wrong answer on the Pretest is *silent,* which may be one characteristic of a BENIGN person, but hardly the major one.

Other forms of the word: BENIGNITY (bə-nig'-nə-tE), n.

CREDULOUS (krej'-ə-ləs) adj.: gullible, overly trusting

The words CREDULOUS, *credible, credence,* and *credit* all come from a Latin word meaning to *believe.* Someone who is CREDULOUS is too easily given to believing something. Such a person might be easily fooled by a tall tale or a lie.

"The CREDULOUS fellow actually believed the two women when they told him about their trip in the flying saucer."

"You are too CREDULOUS. Just because one of your friends says something, that doesn't mean it has to be true."

CREDULOUS is difficult mainly because of confusion with its opposite, *incredulous* (see Chapter 11). People who are *incredulous* of something do not believe in it; they are skeptical or suspicious. *Incredulous* is more commonly used than CREDULOUS, and that may be why so many people pick *suspicious* as the meaning of CREDULOUS.

Other forms of the word: CREDULITY, n.

PARADIGM (par'-ə-dIm or par'-ə-dim) n.: a model, example, pattern

The prefix *para-* means "alongside," as in the word *parallel.* The *digm* part of PARADIGM comes from a Greek word meaning to *show* or *display.* A PARADIGM is a model or pattern of something else. The word tends to have an academic or scientific flavor.

"In the classic conditioned-response PARADIGM, the dog that hears a bell ring whenever he receives food will eventually salivate when he hears the bell, even without receiving food."

"They were considered the PARADIGMS of artistic perfection."

"Shakespeare's Macbeth is a PARADIGM of the man destroyed by his ambition."

The most popular wrong answers are *story* and *lesson,* perhaps suggested by the word *parable.*

Other forms of the word: PARADIGMATIC (par-ə-dig-mat'-ik), adj.

SEQUESTER (si-kwes'-tər) v.: to isolate, segregate, seclude

SEQUESTER means to *set apart,* to *isolate.* Often the sense of the word is "to withdraw into seclusion or solitude."

"His ranch is SEQUESTERED in the California mountains, far from the city."

"The judge SEQUESTERED the jury, putting them in a hotel at night."

"The strange man SEQUESTERED himself in his room and refused to have anything more to do with the world."

In legal usage, SEQUESTER means "to seize property by public authority until legal claims are satisfied," to *confiscate.*

"The estate of the deceased multimillionaire was SEQUESTERED while various parties contested his will."

Other forms of the word: SEQUESTRATION, n.

STODGY (stoj'-E) adj.: dull, pompous, stuffy

STODGY comes from the word *stodge*, which is any thick food, like oatmeal. STODGY can mean *thick* or *heavy*, like *stodge*, but it is usually used in an extended sense to mean *dull, stuffy*, "lacking in humor or lightness."

>   "The STODGY teacher disapproved of students talking and laughing in the corridor."
>   "Susan thought the reception was terribly STODGY— just a bunch of serious people standing around, talking quietly."
>   "Classical music isn't always STODGY; some of it is quite exciting."

The difficulty people have with this word is thinking that it means *old*. An old person, of course, can be the very opposite of STODGY.

SUFFUSE (sə-fyUz') v.: to overspread, spread through

The *-fuse* part of SUFFUSE comes from a Latin word meaning to *pour*. This root is also found in *infuse, diffuse,* and *transfuse*. To SUFFUSE is to overspread, especially with a liquid or a color.

>   "The sunset SUFFUSED the western sky with purple and gold."
>   "Her eyes were SUFFUSED with tears as she remembered her late husband."
>   "Chekhov's plays are SUFFUSED with an air of wistful melancholy."

Other forms of the word: SUFFUSIVE, adj.
SUFFUSION, n.

CELERITY (sə-ler'-ə-tE) n.: swiftness, quickness, rapidity

CELERITY comes from the Latin word for *speed*, also the source of *accelerate*; it is a rather literary synonym for *swiftness, quickness*.

>   "The CELERITY of his response showed that he had mastered the subject."
>   "Art finished his homework with astonishing CELERITY so that he could watch his favorite TV program."
>   "The experienced surgeon performed the operation with ease and CELERITY."

Smoothness is the most common wrong answer, perhaps suggested by the sound of CELERITY, and a confusion of quick movements with smooth ones.

ABLUTION (ə-blU'-shən) n.: a cleansing or washing of the body

An ABLUTION is a washing of the body, particularly as part of a religious rite. It is usually used in the plural.

>   "The novices had to perform their ABLUTIONS before they were allowed to wear the sacred vestments of the priesthood."

ABLUTION is only occasionally used about washing of the body in general.

>   "After Bill had finished his morning ABLUTIONS he felt much better."

ABRADE (ə-brAd') v.: to wear away, erode, scrape, chafe

ABRADE is related to the word ABRASIVE. To ABRADE is to rub or wear away, usually as the result of friction.

>   "The skin on her knees was ABRADED when she slid along the concrete."
>   "The sandpaper ABRADED the surface of the dish."

ABRADE is also sometimes used figuratively, meaning to *wear down* or *irritate*.

>   "Our nerves were ABRADED by the constant noise of the jackhammer outside our window."

Other forms of the word: ABRASION, n.
ABRASIVE, adj.

ABSTRUSE (ab-strUs') adj.: hard to understand, obscure, mysterious

ABSTRUSE means "difficult to understand," usually because of extreme complexity, or because of the remoteness of the material from everyday experience. The word occasionally has a slightly negative sense, suggesting that this complexity may be unnecessary or excessive.

>   "Modern physics is a very ABSTRUSE subject. You have to be an expert to understand much of it."
>   "No one in the audience could make sense of the play's ABSTRUSE symbolism."
>   "The senator's arguments were so ABSTRUSE that no one else on the committee could follow them."

Exercise 1

Answer each question with a YES or NO. Put a check in the space for YES or NO next to each question.

		Yes	No
1.	Would a gentleman VILIFY a friend?	_____	_____
2.	Does a person who fasts practice ABNEGATION?	_____	_____
3.	Are stubborn people AMENABLE to change?	_____	_____
4.	Is an ASCETIC likely to be overweight?	_____	_____
5.	Would a BELLICOSE person be likely to have a large circle of friends?	_____	_____
6.	Is a BENIGN tumor dangerous?	_____	_____
7.	Are skeptics CREDULOUS?	_____	_____
8.	Could a person be a PARADIGM?	_____	_____
9.	Would a hermit want to SEQUESTER himself?	_____	_____
10.	Are most children STODGY?	_____	_____
11.	Can a room be SUFFUSED with light?	_____	_____
12.	Should a typist possess CELERITY?	_____	_____
13.	Could a bath be a form of ABLUTION?	_____	_____
14.	Can sandpaper ABRADE metal?	_____	_____
15.	Can a poem be ABSTRUSE?	_____	_____

Exercise 2

Each sentence contains a test word in CAPITAL letters. Decide whether the test word is being used correctly or incorrectly in the sentence. Put a check in the space for RIGHT or WRONG next to the sentence.

		Right	Wrong
1.	He claimed the magazine was VILIFYING him, but the editor said it was legitimate criticism.	_____	_____
2.	The woman's entire life was one of SELF-ABNEGATION; she always helped others before thinking of herself.	_____	_____
3.	Jake's boss was not AMENABLE to any of the suggestions he made.	_____	_____
4.	Their ASCETIC practices included eating only one meal a day.	_____	_____
5.	The BELLICOSE comedian had us rolling in the aisles with laughter.	_____	_____
6.	His vacation had a BENIGN effect: he came back rested, refreshed, and eager to work.	_____	_____
7.	It is a CREDULOUS story; we are inclined to believe it.	_____	_____
8.	The minister gave his sermon on the PARADIGM of the loaves and the fishes.	_____	_____
9.	She longed to live in a SEQUESTERED village deep in some hidden valley.	_____	_____

10. No one could accuse Mr. Wilkes of being STODGY; he was the life of every party. _____ _____

11. They SUFFUSED us about their true reason for coming here. _____ _____

12. The CELERITY of the surface made the dish difficult to grip. _____ _____

13. They performed their ABLUTIONS with water from a nearby stream. _____ _____

14. She ABRADED us constantly for our poor performance in school. _____ _____

15. It was ABSTRUSE of him to treat me that way; he should be ashamed of himself. _____ _____

Exercise 3

Each test word is followed by three other words. Decide which of the three words is LEAST CLOSELY RELATED in its meaning to the meaning of the test word. Put the letter for the word you choose in the space at the end of the line.

EXAMPLE

	TINY:	**a)** small	**b)** short	**c)** angry	C
1.	VILIFY:	**a)** defame	**b)** malign	**c)** belie	_____
2.	ABNEGATION:	**a)** sacrifice	**b)** prayer	**c)** denial	_____
3.	AMENABLE:	**a)** docile	**b)** pleasant	**c)** responsible	_____
4.	ASCETIC:	**a)** disciplined	**b)** austere	**c)** serene	_____
5.	BELLICOSE:	**a)** noisy	**b)** argumentative	**c)** aggressive	_____
6.	BENIGN:	**a)** humane	**b)** cordial	**c)** tireless	_____
7.	CREDULOUS:	**a)** trusting	**b)** trustworthy	**c)** gullible	_____
8.	PARADIGM:	**a)** example	**b)** character	**c)** standard	_____
9.	SEQUESTER:	**a)** seclude	**b)** destroy	**c)** confiscate	_____
10.	STODGY:	**a)** boring	**b)** prudish	**c)** learned	_____
11.	SUFFUSE:	**a)** saturate	**b)** imbue	**c)** darken	_____
12.	CELERITY:	**a)** softness	**b)** fleetness	**c)** briskness	_____
13.	ABLUTION:	**a)** washing	**b)** cleansing	**c)** beautifying	_____
14.	ABRADE:	**a)** scrape	**b)** puncture	**c)** irritate	_____
15.	ABSTRUSE:	**a)** obscure	**b)** complicated	**c)** ancient	_____

Review Test—Chapters 10–12

Fill in each blank with the test word (or a form of the test word) which best fits the
sentence. Use the words listed below.

ABRADE	ASSIDUOUS	IGNOMINIOUS	PARADIGM	STODGY
ABSTRUSE	CREDULOUS	IMPLACABLE	PRODIGIOUS	SUFFUSE
AMENABLE	ESCHEW	INCOMMODE	PROPINQUITY	TRIBULATION
APPRISE	EXPIATION	INCREDULOUS	PROPITIOUS	UBIQUITOUS
ASCETIC	EXTANT			

1. The _____ mechanic worked hard to make sure the engine was absolutely perfect.

2. All the circumstances were _____ for a victory: everyone was healthy, we were on our home field and we had an excellent game plan.

3. The _____ young man chose to live on bread and water in order to purify his spirit.

4. You are too _____; why do you believe everything you are told?

5. Only the most brilliant students could follow the professor's _____ lecture.

6. As he slid down the side of the hill, his palms were _____ by the rough surface of the rock.

7. Gandhi's movement was a(n) _____ of the successful, nonviolent approach to political change.

8. The townspeople demanded that Hester Prynne wear a scarlet A on her chest as _____ for her adultery.

9. The general's _____ defeat in the important battle destroyed his reputation.

10. The Andersons seemed rather _____ to Barbara; they didn't approve of young people laughing or playing in the house.

11. Jason proved to be extremely _____ to our advice; in fact, he said it was quite helpful.

12. The writer's output was _____: he wrote over a hundred novels in his lifetime.

13. We left the "Do Not Disturb" sign on the door so that the maid wouldn't _____ us.

14. Since absolute silence was required, we were asked to _____ talking during the performances.

15. Despite all her _____ she still managed to keep smiling.

16. Juan wrote us a letter to _____ us of conditions in his country.

17. Nothing would satisfy the _____ enemy but our complete and utter defeat.

18. The evening sky was _____ with an eerie red glow.

19. You couldn't go anywhere in Rome that summer without running into the _____ tourists - cameras and guidebooks in hand.

20. The _____ students refused to believe their teacher could actually make a mistake.

21. The _____ of his apartment to where he worked meant that he could be on the job in less than five minutes.

22. There is only one copy of the book _____; all the rest were destroyed by fire.

Fill in each blank with the test word (or a form of the test word) which best fits the sentence. Use the words listed below.

ABLUTION   BELIE   FERAL   PAROXYSM   SINUOUS
ABNEGATION   BELLICOSE   HIRSUTE   PERFIDY   TENABLE
ADMONISH   BENIGN   INIQUITOUS   RUMINATE   VILIFY
ANCILLARY   CELERITY   INVECTIVE   SEQUESTER   VOLUBLE
ANOMALY   FATUOUS   ONEROUS

23. The speech was totally _____; there wasn't an ounce of sense in it.

24. The task of retyping the book proved to be too _____ for just one person, so two people were assigned to it.

25. His views on medicine are simply not _____ in light of what we know about how the body works.

26. We were impressed by her act of _____: she refused to accept any financial rewards for her medical discovery.

27. The animal's _____ instincts told it when it was in danger.

28. After a year without a shave or haircut, Jim had an extremely _____ appearance.

29. We have enough money for the required equipment, but not for the _____ materials that would make the job so much easier.

30. The _____ uncle would always have a kind word and a gift for his nephews and nieces.

31. She works with such great _____ that she will finish the job by the end of the day.

32. The _____ actress spent half an hour answering the interviewer's first question.

33. The newspaper _____ the mayor, saying that he was the scum of the earth.

34. The committee was _____ in the conference room all day while they tried to decide whom to hire.

35. The newspaper called the dictator's decision _____, a disgraceful violation of human rights.

36. The audience went into a sudden _____ of laughter when the comedian told the joke.

37. The man _____ Jimmy for disturbing his nap.

38. His insistence on wearing a business suit and tie made him a(n) _____ among the casually dressed students.

39. Late at night he liked to _____ on what his life would have been like if he had been born in another century.

40. The _____ man said that if anyone disagreed with him, he'd be happy to prove his point with his fists.

41. We were astonished by his _____ in selling the military secrets to the enemy.

42. Your trembling hands _____ your brave words; you are really quite frightened.

43. The _____ path of the stream led us in and out of many interesting places.

44. The priestess performed a ceremonial _____ by washing her face and hands in the sacred water.

45. The writer's speech was filled with _____; we were shocked at the bitterness of his insults.

Common Prefixes

A *prefix* is one or more syllables placed at the beginning of a word that change or add to its meaning. Only some of the more common prefixes have been listed here. Note that many prefixes have more than one spelling. Also note that prefixes may have more than one meaning. Only the most important ones are given here; check your dictionary for other meanings.

Prefix	Meaning	Examples
A-, also AN-	not; without	ANonymous: without a name
AB-, also ABS-	away from	ABsent: away, not present
AD-, also A followed by two consonants	to; toward	ADhere: to stick to ATTract: to pull toward
ANTI-	against	ANTIslavery: against slavery
CON-, also COM-, COL-, CO-, COR-	with; together	CONnect: to join together COMbine: to mix together
DE-	down from; away from; not	DEpart: to go away DEpress: to press down on, make sad
DIS-, also DI-	apart; away; not	DISmiss: to send away DIShonest: not honest
EX-, also E-	out of; from	EXclaim: to shout out Emerge: to come out
1. IN-, also IL-, IM-, IR-	in; into	INsert: to put in IMport: to bring into (a country)
2. IN-, also IL-, IM-, IR-	not	INformal: not formal ILlegal: not legal
INTER-	between; among	INTERrupt: to break into the middle of INTERnational: among nations
MIS-	badly; wrong; not	MIStreat: to treat badly MIStake: a wrong answer
NON-	not	NONbeliever: not a believer NONstop: not stopping

Prefix	Meaning	Examples
PRE-	before; early; in advance	PREpare: to get ready beforehand PREhistoric: before history
PRO-	in front of; forward; in favor of	PROceed: to go forward PROminent: standing out; easily seen
RE-	back; again	REfund: to pay back REsume: to begin again
SUB-	under; below	SUBmarine: a ship that can travel under water
SUPER-	over; above; beyond	SUPERvise: to watch over SUPERhuman: beyond human strength or ability
TRANS-, also TRA-	across; beyond; through	TRANSparent: able to be seen through TRANSoceanic: crossing the ocean; beyond the ocean
UN-	not; opposite of	UNhappy: not happy UNlock: to do the opposite of locking

Common Suffixes

A *suffix* is one or more syllables added to the end of a word to change or add to its meaning. As with the prefix list, only the more common ones have been listed here. Note that an important job of a suffix—and sometimes its only job—is to show the part of speech of the word to which it is attached.

Suffix	Meaning	Examples	Part of Speech
-ABLE, also -IBLE	able to; tending to; having	breakABLE: able to be broken valuABLE: having value	adjective
-AL	connected with; like	originAL: connected with the beginning monumentAL: like a monument	adjective
-ANT, also -ENT	doing; being	pleasANT: being pleasing differENT: not being the same	adjective
1. -ATE	to make; to act; to cause	abbreviATE: to make shorter activATE: to cause to become active	verb
2. -ATE	being	adequATE: being enough	adjective
-ER, also -OR	one that is; one that does	foreignER: one who is foreign actOR: one who acts	noun
-FUL	full of; able to	beautiFUL: full of beauty harmFUL: able to harm	adjective
-FY, also -IFY	to make; to cause; to be	simplIFY: to make simple liqueFY: to make liquid	verb
-IC, also -ICAL	like; being	metallIC: being metal fanatICAL: like a fanatic	adjective
-ISH	like; somewhat	childISH: like a child reddISH: somewhat red	adjective
-ITY	a state; condition	insanITY: the state of being insane	noun
-IVE	connected with; having a tendency toward	actIVE: tending to be full of action festIVE: like a festival	adjective

Suffix	Meaning	Examples	Part of Speech
-LESS	without; unable to be done	fatherLESS: without a father countLESS: unable to be counted	adjective
-MENT	a state; condition; result	amazeMENT: the state of being amazed attachMENT: the result of attaching	noun
-NESS	a quality; state	darkNESS: the state of being dark goodNESS: the quality of being good	noun
-OUS	full of; having; like	courageOUS: having courage joyOUS: full of joy	adjective
-TUDE	a state; condition	gratiTUDE: the state of being thankful	noun
-Y	full of; having; inclined to	greedY: full of greed dreamY: inclined to dream	adjective

Answers—WORDBOOK 7

Chapter 1

		Pretest	Exercise 1	Exercise 2	Exercise 3
1.	ABASE:	degrade	N	W	c
2.	MALIGN:	slander	N	W	a
3.	OVERT:	unconcealed	Y	W	b
4.	DEBONAIR:	carefree	N	R	b
5.	INSOLVENT:	bankrupt	N	R	c
6.	RESPITE:	pause	Y	R	a
7.	ROTUND:	plump	N	R	a
8.	HOVEL:	hut	Y	R	a
9.	INORDINATE:	excessive	N	R	c
10.	INTRACTABLE:	stubborn	Y	W	b
11.	MANIFEST:	apparent	Y	R	b
12.	VERTIGO:	dizziness	Y	R	a
13.	CONDUCIVE:	favorable	N	R	c
14.	DISCONCERT:	confuse	Y	R	b
15.	INFUSE:	fill	Y	R	c

Chapter 2

		Pretest	Exercise 1	Exercise 2	Exercise 3
1.	PREDISPOSED:	inclined	N	W	a
2.	REPROVE:	rebuke	N	R	c
3.	SUBTERFUGE:	deception	Y	R	b
4.	ACQUIESCE:	agree	Y	R	a
5.	ACRIMONIOUS:	bitter	N	R	b
6.	COPIOUS:	plentiful	N	R	c
7.	FURTIVE:	secret	Y	R	a
8.	HARBINGER:	forerunner	Y	R	a
9.	INCLEMENT:	stormy	N	R	c
10.	PORTENT:	omen	Y	R	c
11.	ADVERSITY:	hardship	Y	R	c
12.	COGITATE:	ponder	N	W	b
13.	CORPULENT:	fat	Y	R	a
14.	DERISIVE:	mocking	Y	R	b
15.	DISCONSOLATE:	heartbroken	Y	W	c

Chapter 3

		Pretest	Exercise 1	Exercise 2	Exercise 3
1.	EXACERBATE:	aggravate	Y	W	b
2.	FELICITY:	happiness	N	R	c
3.	OBLIVIOUS:	forgetful	Y	R	b
4.	SQUALOR:	filthiness	N	R	c
5.	AFFRAY:	brawl	Y	W	a
6.	ANTIPATHY:	aversion	N	W	a
7.	ASPECT:	appearance	Y	R	a
8.	CONTRITION:	repentance	Y	W	c
9.	IMPUDENT:	shameless	Y	R	a
10.	INDOLENT:	lazy	N	R	a
11.	INTERLOPER:	intruder	N	R	a
12.	MILIEU:	surroundings	Y	R	a
13.	NEBULOUS:	hazy	Y	W	b
14.	ODIOUS:	hateful	Y	W	c
15.	REPAST:	meal	Y	W	c

Chapter 4

		Pretest	Exercise 1	Exercise 2	Exercise 3
1.	ASCRIBE:	attribute	Y	W	c
2.	AUSPICIOUS:	favorable	N	W	b
3.	GLOWER:	scowl	N	R	b
4.	GUILE:	trickiness	Y	R	a
5.	OBDURATE:	stubborn	N	R	c
6.	PARITY:	equality	Y	R	a
7.	PAUCITY:	scarcity	Y	W	b
8.	TRANSGRESS:	violate	Y	W	c
9.	TRAVAIL:	toil	N	W	c
10.	WAN:	sickly	N	R	c
11.	COMMISERATE:	sympathize	N	W	c
12.	DISCERN:	notice	Y	R	b
13.	PONDEROUS:	heavy	N	R	b
14.	SHIFTLESS:	lazy	N	R	a
15.	AMITY:	friendship	N	R	c

Chapter 5

		Pretest	Exercise 1	Exercise 2	Exercise 3
1.	GERMANE:	relevant	N	R	a
2.	GIBE:	jeer	Y	R	c
3.	INIMITABLE:	matchless	Y	W	b
4.	ITINERANT:	journeying	N	R	b
5.	MELLIFLUOUS:	sweet-sounding	Y	R	b
6.	PUGNACIOUS:	quarrelsome	Y	W	a
7.	AFICIONADO:	enthusiast	N	R	a
8.	CEDE:	give up	Y	W	a
9.	DEBASE:	corrupt	Y	W	c
10.	FOMENT:	stir up	Y	R	c
11.	FORBEARANCE:	patience	N	R	b
12.	JOCOSE:	humorous	N	R	c
13.	VEX:	annoy	Y	R	b
14.	BURGEON:	develop	Y	W	a
15.	DISTEND:	swell	Y	R	c

Chapter 6

		Pretest	Exercise 1	Exercise 2	Exercise 3
1.	INTIMATION:	suggestion	N	R	b
2.	INVIOLATE:	intact	Y	R	a
3.	LUMINARY:	celebrity	Y	R	c
4.	PANACHE:	flair	Y	R	a
5.	PARRY:	ward off	N	R	c
6.	SURREPTITIOUS:	secret	Y	W	a
7.	UPBRAID:	scold	Y	R	c
8.	DISPARATE:	unlike	Y	W	a
9.	PECUNIARY:	monetary	Y	R	a
10.	PROVISO:	stipulation	Y	R	a
11.	REMISS:	careless	Y	R	b
12.	STIGMA:	stain	Y	R	c
13.	TRUNCATE:	cut short	Y	R	a
14.	VAPID:	lifeless	Y	R	b
15.	ABSTEMIOUS:	sparing	N	R	a

Chapter 7

		Pretest	Exercise 1	Exercise 2	Exercise 3
1.	FLACCID:	flabby	N	W	c
2.	DAUNT:	discourage	Y	R	a
3.	MESMERIZE:	hypnotize	Y	W	b
4.	PEEVISH:	irritable	N	R	b
5.	PRODIGY:	marvel	Y	W	b
6.	TENET:	belief	Y	R	a
7.	DOLOROUS:	mournful	Y	R	b
8.	FRETFUL:	irritable	N	W	c
9.	PROGENY:	descendants	Y	R	b
10.	AMBIENCE:	environment	Y	R	c
11.	CATACLYSM:	disaster	Y	R	c
12.	DEMISE:	death	Y	R	a
13.	HINTERLAND:	backcountry	N	R	a
14.	IMBROGLIO:	predicament	Y	R	a
15.	MISCREANT:	evildoer	Y	R	c

Chapter 8

		Pretest	Exercise 1	Exercise 2	Exercise 3
1.	QUAFF:	drink	N	R	b
2.	CHOLERIC:	bad tempered	N	W	b
3.	DULCET:	sweet	Y	W	a
4.	OBSEQUIOUS:	fawning	N	R	b
5.	REMUNERATE:	pay	Y	W	b
6.	TIMOROUS:	fearful	N	R	b
7.	CHURLISH:	rude	N	R	c
8.	DILATE:	expand	Y	W	c
9.	HIATUS:	gap	Y	R	b
10.	LASSITUDE:	weariness	Y	W	a
11.	PETULANT:	irritable	N	R	b
12.	REVERIE:	daydream	N	W	b
13.	SAGACIOUS:	shrewd	N	R	a
14.	DIRE:	fearful	Y	R	a
15.	EBULLIENCE:	enthusiasm	N	R	b

Chapter 9

		Pretest	Exercise 1	Exercise 2	Exercise 3
1.	HAPLESS:	unlucky	Y	R	a
2.	INCULCATE:	instill	Y	W	a
3.	INFINITESIMAL:	tiny	N	R	c
4.	NOXIOUS:	harmful	Y	R	a
5.	PARSIMONIOUS:	stingy	N	W	a
6.	POTABLE:	drinkable	N	R	c
7.	VOCIFEROUS:	clamorous	N	R	a
8.	ABJECT:	wretched	Y	R	a
9.	BLITHE:	joyful	N	R	a
10.	CATARACT:	waterfall	Y	R	b
11.	OBFUSCATE:	obscure	N	W	b
12.	OBSTREPEROUS:	unruly	N	R	a
13.	OSSIFY:	harden	N	W	c
14.	PORTEND:	forebode	Y	W	c
15.	PROTRACT:	prolong	Y	W	a

Chapter 10

		Pretest	Exercise 1	Exercise 2	Exercise 3
1.	ANCILLARY:	auxiliary	N	R	a
2.	BELIE:	contradict	Y	R	a
3.	INIQUITOUS:	wicked	N	R	c
4.	PROPINQUITY:	nearness	Y	R	c
5.	TENABLE:	defensible	N	R	a
6.	ASSIDUOUS:	diligent	N	R	b
7.	ESCHEW:	shun	Y	R	c
8.	PERFIDY:	treachery	Y	R	b
9.	PRODIGIOUS:	huge	Y	W	c
10.	SINUOUS:	curving	Y	W	b
11.	UBIQUITOUS:	omnipresent	Y	W	c
12.	APPRISE:	inform	Y	W	b
13.	EXPIATION:	atonement	Y	R	a
14.	EXTANT:	existing	N	R	b
15.	FATUOUS:	foolish	N	W	b

Chapter 11

		Pretest	Exercise 1	Exercise 2	Exercise 3
1.	INCOMMODE:	disturb	Y	W	c
2.	INCREDULOUS:	skeptical	Y	W	b
3.	INVECTIVE:	abuse	Y	R	a
4.	ONEROUS:	burdensome	Y	W	b
5.	PROPITIOUS:	favorable	Y	R	a
6.	RUMINATE:	meditate	N	W	a
7.	ADMONISH:	warn	N	W	b
8.	HIRSUTE:	hairy	Y	R	b
9.	IGNOMINIOUS:	humiliating	N	W	c
10.	IMPLACABLE:	relentless	N	R	a
11.	VOLUBLE:	talkative	Y	W	a
12.	ANOMALY:	irregularity	Y	W	a
13.	FERAL:	wild	N	R	c
14.	PAROXYSM:	spasm	N	R	a
15.	TRIBULATION:	suffering	Y	W	c

Chapter 12

		Pretest	Exercise 1	Exercise 2	Exercise 3
1.	VILIFY:	slander	N	R	c
2.	ABNEGATION:	self-denial	Y	R	b
3.	AMENABLE:	submissive	N	R	b
4.	ASCETIC:	austere	N	R	c
5.	BELLICOSE:	warlike	N	W	a
6.	BENIGN:	kindly	N	R	c
7.	CREDULOUS:	gullible	N	W	b
8.	PARADIGM:	model	Y	W	b
9.	SEQUESTER:	isolate	Y	R	b
10.	STODGY:	dull	N	R	c
11.	SUFFUSE:	overspread	Y	W	c
12.	CELERITY:	swiftness	Y	W	a
13.	ABLUTION:	cleansing	Y	R	c
14.	ABRADE:	wear away	Y	W	b
15.	ABSTRUSE:	mysterious	Y	W	c

Review Test 1

1. affray
2. subterfuges
3. harbinger
4. antipathy
5. furtive
6. conducive
7. repast
8. adversities
9. acrimonious
10. debonair
11. hovel
12. indolent
13. exacerbate
14. overt
15. inordinate
16. rotund
17. copious *or* inordinate
18. maligned
19. infused
20. felicity
21. acquiesce
22. milieu
23. inclement
24. portent
25. disconcerted
26. insolvent
27. manifest
28. impudent
29. intractable
30. corpulent
31. disconsolate
32. nebulous
33. aspect
34. contrition
35. predisposed
36. squalor
37. oblivious
38. vertigo
39. cogitate
40. interloper
41. derisive
42. odious
43. respite
44. reproved
45. abase

Review Test 2

1. jocose
2. truncate
3. vexed
4. amity
5. inviolate
6. inimitable
7. discern
8. proviso
9. upbraided
10. obdurate
11. mellifluous
12. travail
13. paucity
14. gibed
15. shiftless
16. parity
17. transgressed
18. auspicious
19. guile
20. parry
21. surreptitious
22. remiss
23. ponderous
24. foment
25. germane
26. burgeon
27. commiserated
28. itinerant
29. distended
30. pugnacious
31. wan
32. disparate
33. ascribe
34. debase
35. intimation
36. pecuniary
37. glowered
38. forbearance
39. vapid
40. cede
41. aficionado
42. luminaries
43. stigma
44. abstemious
45. panache

Review Test 3

1. inculcate
2. miscreant
3. prodigy
4. obfuscate
5. daunted
6. protract
7. tenets
8. reverie
9. infinitesimal
10. hiatus
11. imbroglio
12. churlish
13. remunerate
14. sagacious
15. mesmerized
16. quaff
17. fretful *or* churlish
18. parsimonious
19. cataclysms
20. demise
21. abject
22. progeny
23. ambience
24. portended
25. ossified
26. flaccid
27. dolorous
28. petulant *or* peevish *or* obstreperous
29. potable
30. peevish *or* petulant *or* choleric
31. vociferous *or* obstreperous
32. blithe *or* ebullient
33. dulcet
34. cataract
35. timorous
36. noxious
37. choleric *or* peevish *or* petulant
38. obstreperous *or* vociferous
39. dire
40. ebullience
41. hapless
42. lassitude
43. obsequious
44. dilates
45. hinterland

Review Test 4

1. assiduous
2. propitious
3. ascetic
4. credulous
5. abstruse
6. abraded
7. paradigm
8. expiation
9. ignominious
10. stodgy
11. amenable
12. prodigious
13. incommode
14. eschew
15. tribulations
16. apprise
17. implacable
18. suffused
19. ubiquitous
20. incredulous
21. propinquity
22. extant
23. fatuous
24. onerous
25. tenable
26. abnegation
27. feral
28. hirsute
29. ancillary
30. benign
31. celerity
32. voluble
33. vilified
34. sequestered
35. iniquitous
36. paroxysm
37. admonished
38. anomaly
39. ruminate
40. bellicose
41. perfidy
42. belie
43. sinuous
44. ablution
45. invective

Index—WORDBOOK 7

The number after each word indicates the chapter in which the word is treated.

Abase, 1
Abject, 9
Ablution, 12
Abnegation, 12
Abrade, 12
Abstemious, 6
Abstruse, 12
Acquiesce, 2
Acrimonious, 2
Admonish, 11
Adversity, 2
Affray, 3
Aficionado, 5
Ambience, 7
Amenable, 12
Amity, 4
Ancillary, 10
Anomaly, 11
Antipathy, 3
Apprise, 10
Ascetic, 12
Ascribe, 4
Aspect, 3
Assiduous, 10
Auspicious, 4

Belie, 10
Bellicose, 12
Benign, 12
Blithe, 9
Burgeon, 5

Cataclysm, 7
Cataract, 9

Cede, 5
Celerity, 12
Choleric, 8
Churlish, 8
Cogitate, 2
Commiserate, 4
Conducive, 1
Contrition, 3
Copious, 2
Corpulent, 2
Credulous, 12

Daunt, 7
Debase, 5
Debonair, 1
Demise, 7
Derisive, 2
Dilate, 8
Dire, 8
Discern, 4
Disconcert, 1
Disconsolate, 2
Disparate, 6
Distend, 5
Dolorous, 7
Dulcet, 8

Ebullience, 8
Eschew, 10
Exacerbate, 3
Expiation, 10
Extant, 10

Fatuous, 10
Felicity, 3
Feral, 11
Flaccid, 7
Foment, 5
Forbearance, 5
Fretful, 7
Furtive, 2

Germane, 5
Gibe, 5
Glower, 4
Guile, 4

Hapless, 9
Harbinger, 2
Hiatus, 8
Hinterland, 7
Hirsute, 11
Hovel, 1

Ignominious, 11
Imbroglio, 7
Implacable, 11
Impudent, 3
Inclement, 2
Incommode, 11
Incredulous, 11
Inculcate, 9
Indolent, 3
Infinitesimal, 9
Infuse, 1
Inimitable, 5
Iniquitous, 10

Inordinate, 1
Insolvent, 1
Interloper, 3
Intimation, 6
Intractable, 1
Invective, 11
Inviolate, 6
Itinerant, 5

Jocose, 5

Lassitude, 8
Luminary, 6

Malign, 1
Manifest, 1
Mellifluous, 5
Mesmerize, 7
Milieu, 3
Miscreant, 7

Nebulous, 3
Noxious, 9

Obdurate, 4
Obfuscate, 9
Oblivious, 3
Obsequious, 8
Obstreperous, 9
Odious, 3
Onerous, 11
Ossify, 9
Overt, 1

Panache, 6
Paradigm, 12
Parity, 4
Paroxysm, 11
Parry, 6
Parsimonious, 9
Paucity, 4
Pecuniary, 6
Peevish, 7
Perfidy, 10
Petulant, 8
Ponderous, 4
Portend, 9
Portent, 2
Potable, 9
Predisposed, 2
Prodigious, 10
Prodigy, 7
Progeny, 7
Propinquity, 10
Propitious, 11
Protract, 9
Proviso, 6
Pugnacious, 5

Quaff, 8

Remiss, 6
Remunerate, 8
Repast, 3
Reprove, 2
Respite, 1
Reverie, 8

Rotund, 1
Ruminate, 11

Sagacious, 8
Sequester, 12
Shiftless, 4
Sinuous, 10
Squalor, 3
Stigma, 6
Stodgy, 12
Subterfuge, 2
Suffuse, 12
Surreptitious, 6

Tenable, 10
Tenet, 7
Timorous, 8
Transgress, 4
Travail, 4
Tribulation, 11
Truncate, 6

Ubiquitous, 10
Upbraid, 6

Vapid, 6
Vertigo, 1
Vex, 5
Vilify, 12
Vociferous, 9
Voluble, 11

Wan, 4

Vocabulary Review List

On this page you can list words from the *Wordbook* that gave you particular difficulty, so that you can continue to review them. You might also wish to include in the list difficult words that you come across in your reading. The sample sentence may be one you make up yourself, a sentence from the *Wordbook* discussion, or a sentence from your reading. It should clearly illustrate how the word is used. This page can be removed from the *Wordbook* and placed in a notebook or three-ring binder for easy reference.

Word	Definition	Sample Sentence
COURTEOUS	polite, well-mannered	The COURTEOUS boy held the door open for his mother.

Word   **Definition**   **Sample Sentence**

_____   _____   _____

_____   _____   _____

_____   _____   _____

_____   _____   _____

_____   _____   _____

_____   _____   _____

_____   _____   _____

_____   _____   _____

_____   _____   _____

_____   _____   _____

_____   _____   _____

_____   _____   _____

_____   _____   _____

_____   _____   _____

_____   _____   _____